EIGHT LIGHTS

EIGHT

BY WILLIAM F. AND ROBERT J. ROSENBLUM

ILLUSTRATED BY SHRAGA WEIL

LIGHTS

THE STORY OF CHANUKAH

DOUBLEDAY & COMPANY, INC.

GARDEN CITY, NEW YORK

1967

Library of Congress Catalog Card Number 67-12543
Copyright © 1967 William F. Rosenblum and Robert J. Rosenblum
Printed in the United States of America
First Edition

INTRODUCTION

THE CHANUKAH STORY

In every age world events give new meaning to old epics. The Revelation of the Law at Sinai, the winning of the Magna Charta, the Declaration of Independence, The Gettysburg Address, reflecting decisive moments in history, events which changed the destinies of men and nations, have assumed new moral stature in the eyes of the world because of the struggle everywhere of the underprivileged for their rightful place in the sun, because of the demand of the victims of oppression to be free.

One truth stands out in undimmed clarity—each generation which inherits the liberties which have been won by those who have gone before has to win them all over again. It too has to pay the price of eternal vigilance and continuous sacrifice to make certain that freedom is preserved. And it is when we rehearse the trials which our forebears endured and the triumphs which they achieved that we gain the resolve and the strength to go forward to victory ourselves.

The account of the war of the ancient Maccabees against the Syrian Antiochus Epiphanes is therefore of momentous significance to our generation, to people of all creeds, to people of all countries. Although featured in the Jewish religious calendar, it has a message which is as universal as the globe and as eternal as all time. The victory of Judah Maccabee and his small band of zealots is commemorated in the festival of Chanukah. Until recently, it was treated as a minor holiday but events in many parts of the world today have ascribed to this Feast of Lights a new importance and a new impact.

Man has always fought for freedom, not only for liberation from

7

political tyranny or economic enslavement or the right to worship God in his own way, but for emancipation from the burdens and boredom of physical darkness as well. These have been as irksome and intolerable to him as any other tyranny. It was natural, therefore, for Judaism to utilize the epic of the Maccabean triumph during the season of the winter solstice to stress and proclaim our passion for light, our determination that the divine lamp of liberty shall never go out, that it will penetrate every encircling gloom.

There are few chapters in the annals of mankind as striking as the War of the Maccabees. Palestine had been the crossroads of the ancient Middle East for centuries. The descendants of Abraham, Isaac and Jacob who dwelt there after the exodus from Egypt had few periods of respite from war and invasion. One of the most oppressive interruptions to their peace came with the conquest of Palestine by Alexander the Great in the fourth century B.C.E. It brought in its wake not only Greek control but Greek culture, a heathen, voluptuous way of life in distinct contrast to the rigorous and disciplined moral conduct prescribed by the Mosaic code. As was to be anticipated, many of the Jewish officials and many of the prominent and affluent in Judea, in their eagerness to curry favor with the minions of Alexander, adopted the manners and the mores of the new rulers. They let their Hebrew loyalties wane at the onset of Hellenization, especially so in the capital city of Jerusalem and in the larger communities of the land.

True, this had happened before. Early in their history the children of Israel, then the conquerors, when they occupied Canaan, had allowed many of the practices of the Philistines to infiltrate their own but they gave them new interpretations, seeking to harmonize them with the tenets of their Mosaic faith which they would not desert. The prophets cried out against these "idolatries" but to many it appeared as a natural process of syncretism. Now, as the defeated, all too many in Judea abandoned themselves to the pagan rites and persuasions of their Greek rulers without any pretense of accommodating them to their historic Hebrew religion. They accepted the Greek philosophy of emphasis on physical instead of spiritual power as a mark of character. They dressed like Greeks, disported themselves in the gymnasia like them and even adored the heathen gods. Not a few forsook their observance of the Sabbath and the Holy Days and took on Greek names to manifest their complete surrender to the new masters. This was not religious syncretism. This was spiritual treason—there was no room for a Jewish soul in a Greek body!

These defections did not go unchallenged by the greater number of Jews. Albeit poorer in means and lowlier in position, they were mightier in their steadfastness to the God of their Fathers and to the Law of Sinai. To them the actions of the "Hellenists," those who aped the Greeks, was a brand of cravenness more despicable than cowardice on the field of battle. It engendered in them a seething dismay and burning resentment, a desperate waiting day after day and year after year for the right moment to cast off all caution and vent their wrath upon those who were so quick to sell the birthright of Jacob to the new Esau. That moment was to come. It took nearly two hundred years but destiny takes a long time to perform its wonders.

Unlike the other holidays and Holy Days in the calendar of Judaism, Chanukah is not recorded in a book of the Old Testament nor mentioned in any of its chapters. The story is told in the Apocryphal Book of Maccabees. About 178 B.C.E. a new king arose over Palestine, one Antiochus, a Syrian. Antiochus liked to call himself "Epiphanes," the revealed God. He became known as "Epimanes," the mad man, because of his cruelty and tyranny. He had one mania, above all others—he wanted to mold the various peoples in his realms into "one people," one people who would worship his Greek god Zeus, one people who would become "as Greek as the Greeks." To accomplish this he stooped to every device of duplicity and dictatorship and it was this ambition which led to his downfall and defeat.

Antiochus was as crafty as he was cruel and crass. He knew how to capitalize on the weaknesses of men. He was sure that among the Hebrew priests there would be some who would sell their souls to save their positions and purses. He cajoled, he threatened, he bribed, he haggled until he found the price they would take and he was willing to pay. The most influential office in Judea was that of the High Priest. A leader among the Hellenist Jews, Jason was easily induced to become a servant of Antiochus but a few years later the infamous Menelaus offered a higher sum and the Syrian installed him as High Priest instead. This was a blow to the pride of the Jews. They were outraged. The office of High Priest was to be occupied only by those in the line of family descent. *This was a tradition which even a conqueror dared not ignore.* Jason was at *least of priestly lineage. The corrupt Menelaus was not.* Many Jews were ready now "to do something." And when a report came that Antiochus had been defeated in his battle against Ptolemy of Egypt, this encouraged the Jews in Judea to move against their Greek captors. However, the report proved false and there ensued a campaign of persecution and rapine from which the Jews were not to be relieved until years later in 165 B.C.E., when the War of the Maccabees ended in one of the most amazing victories in the career of the Jews, in fact a victory rare in all the annals of civilization.

The story of Chanukah is indeed one to tell and retell in our day when we are sorely tried and prone to lose heart in the face of the many wrongs and oppressions which still obtain. As one looks back over the centuries and looks out upon our current world, the fate which befell Antiochus gives us new hope that freedom and faith will never perish from the earth. For all tyrants make the same mistakes. In their madness for power they are never content to destroy the physical and material might of their victims but seek to rob them of their religion as well. Some may become afraid or indifferent but many will risk all they own and even their lives in defense of their ideals. This is an axiom of human experience.

When Antiochus decreed that the Temple at Jerusalem, the shrine where "the Lord dwelt in their midst," was to be stripped of every vestige of Judaism and that on the altar where sacrifices were offered to "the Lord of All" a likeness of Zeus was to be enthroned, the dictator made the fatal error which sealed his doom. The psalms of the priests were replaced with pagan incantations while the Holy of

Holies was polluted by vulgar dances and orgies . . . and even those Jews who had been indifferent before were revolted at this "profanation of the Holy Name." All that was needed was someone to lead them—was it not always thus in their history—a Moses, a David, a Solomon—someone was certain to call and they would answer! One did, Mattathias an elder in a small town near Jerusalem.

As we have said, the story of Chanukah should be rehearsed in these our own times, when light is sorely needed in the gathering darkness. On all sides the prophets of disaster insist that mankind is losing faith in the survival of those virtues which set humanity apart from all other of the Lord's creatures. These are false prophets who forget how great is the power of the spirit when aroused, greater than might, making man little lower than the angels and endowing him with strength to perform miracles! Such was the Maccabean epic.

A survey of the history of mankind reveals a dramatic affinity between epochal events and the season in which they occur. We see such concatenation of an event and its "timing" in the celebration of Chanukah, for this is both the Maccabean festival and the Feast of Lights. It takes place when the days are growing shorter and the nights longer and the spirit of man yearns for light.

There was great rejoicing in Judea when, in the closing months of the year 165 B.C.E., after three years of fierce fighting, Judah and his warriors won the final victory over the hosts of Antiochus. It was on the eve of their wonted rites to pray to God for light, the season of the winter solstice when the cold and darkness sometimes tempted them to yield to doubt and despair. "Let us have light," they would pray, and they would kindle the menorahs in the Temple as a witness of their longing for light. Now they saw in their military triumph at this hour a sign from Heaven that God was with them as he had been with their forefathers—A Pillar of Fire by Night. They did not minimize the valor of the Maccabees nor discount their heroic feats on the battlefield, but they saw the hand of God outstretched once more to protect His people. How else could the mighty Syrian army be overcome? Judah and his followers were completely untrained and outnumbered by the legions of "Epimanes," veterans of many campaigns who had vanquished such mighty armies as those of Egypt. In truth it was God who turned the tide and they wanted to thank Him in His house. Even the weaklings who had welcomed Antiochus to the city as conqueror now became overwhelmingly "zealous for the Lord." They, too, could hardly wait to tear down the idol of Zeus which profaned the sanctuary; they, too, were impatient to cleanse the Temple of every shameful sign and symbol.

What added to the ecstasy of all Judea after the years of agony was the knowledge that the rededication would be held at the time they always celebrated their Feast of Lights. What could be more appropriate? Unlike their Greek neighbors, the Judeans did not resort to heathen excesses to implore Heaven to dispel the darkness. They kindled their golden menorahs in the Temple. They flooded the entire sanctuary with lights and sang hymns of praise and thanksgiving unto the Lord, Creator of the Sun, Moon and Stars. They glorified Him for the light of faith which blazed in their hearts and minds even when the skies were not so bright, as at the winter solstice.

So the multitudes streamed to the Temple for a joyous rededication. They would celebrate for eight days and nights, to parallel another festival of freedom in their history, one which recalled the flight of their ancestors from another despot, the Pharaoh of Egypt. There was only one anxiety. There was not enough oil in the holy vessels for eight days, indeed barely enough for one day. Again the hand of God reached out to help and bless His people, for, miracle of miracles, as they continued their hymns of praise and hallelujahs of thanksgiving, the lamps did not flicker or go out. Strangely, their flames grew brighter with the hours and days until, on the last night, the Temple was aglow as never before in all its splendor and magnificence.

Therefore it is enjoined in the Book of Maccabees "that the days of the dedication of the altar be kept in their season from year to year by the space of eight days from the five and twentieth day of the month Kislev with mirth and gladness."

We do not have to delve into the archeologies of the Maccabean period to reconstruct the scene which took place in Jerusalem these twenty-one centuries ago; nor go to the splendid chronicle in the

Apocrypha. We can recapture the "mirth and gladness" with which our ancestors were intoxicated if we but speak today to those of our brothers who have survived the holocaust of the Nazi Epimanes. In their eyes we see reflected the light which freedom kindles in the lives of men, and in their words we hear the sweet music which faith inspires as her song of songs.

Yes, the lesson which the Jewish festival of Chanukah is meant to dramatize is for all God's children—the eternal striving of humanity for the threefold blessing—of light, of faith, of Freedom—without which man is but little higher than the beasts of the field, with which he is but little lower than the angels.

It is a paradox of man's destiny that although he inherits these priceless spiritual possessions from his forebears, he has to secure them for himself all over again, often at the cost of his life. In moments of weakness he can be like Jason and Menelaus and their ilk, who accept the vagaries and vicissitudes of events to save their skins, who are loath to fight for their spiritual heritage or naively persuade themselves that the new patrimony which is dangled before them or forced upon them will be just as good. Or he can be as the Jew has been throughout the ages for the greater part, like a wise and mature Mattathias or a zealous and daring Judah, convinced that there are no substitutes for the treasures of the mind and spirit willed to him by the generations of the past. Strange as it may seem, he knows he has to "buy" what is already his, often with blood and sweat and tears . . . and even his life!

Here the story of Chanukah is brought up to date as a twice-told tale. One recaptures the rededication of the Temple in Jerusalem through the witness of some who were there; the other portrays the Chanukah observance in a synagogue of today and the thoughts of some who are there—a twice-told tale which forms a bridge between the centuries.

The tapers which burn in the menorah in a Jewish home at Chanukah or the more impressive menorah which illumines the synagogue altar are more than a Jewish symbol. They are a challenge to the world to remain zealous in the war against darkness—a warning that the light must never fail!

13

EIGHT LIGHTS

THE
FIRST
NIGHT

It was the twenty-fifth day of Kislev.

On this day, exactly three years past, the Temple had ceased to be. Its walls had not crumbled to dust, the earth upon which it stood had not parted and swallowed up the great structure. And yet, just as surely, the Temple was suddenly no more.

It was the twenty-fifth day of Kislev.

On this same day, three years earlier, Antiochus had sent his men into the Temple to spill the blood of swine as an offering to Zeus. They had come before—these missionaries of Antiochus—to rob the Temple of its golden vessels and candlesticks, to tear down and bear away the hangings woven of golden thread. But this time they had come to profane the Temple, to worship in ways they knew to be forbidden within these sacred walls. And with the flashing of a knife, they had made the stones around them no longer sacred. And the Temple was suddenly no more.

It was the twenty-fifth day of Kislev.

On this day, only three years before, those who had remained faithful to the God of Israel had rent their clothes, and rubbed themselves with ashes and cried aloud in lamentation. And they had prayed, offering together the same prayers which would have been offered at the death of anyone of their kin. For the Temple was no more. Its walls were still standing—even as the body of one whose heartbeat flickers out does not instantly vanish—but within those walls there was darkness. The soul of the Temple had fled into the hearts of its people.

17

Now, at last, exactly three years later, the people had returned to banish the darkness with holy lights. The Temple would be reborn.

Many days had been spent preparing for the last rituals of rededication. The army of believers commanded by Judah Maccabee had fought its way back from the desert wilderness—back to the green valleys, back to their homes, back to Jerusalem, back to the Temple —only to come before a desolate place. The vision of magnificence which each Jew had carried for three years, through battle and through hardship, was gone.

The massive gates of cedar, oiled and rubbed to a high luster, were gone. Only charred remnants remained, clinging with splintery claws to rusty brackets.

The carefully tended courtyards were gone. Instead, thickets of wild bushes and thorny brambles grew everywhere.

The fine polished stones of the sanctuary walls were scarred with obscene drawings, great meandering depictions of the pagan rites which had celebrated the power of Zeus.

The old altar of wood and carefully cut stone had been replaced by crude slabs, darkened now with the blood of hundreds of unclean animals.

And the scrolls were gone, the rolled parchments upon which had been written the heritage of Israel, its history and its Law.

But while ruin confronted them everywhere, the returning Jews did not despair. The vision of the Temple as it once had been did not fade. And with this picture of ancient glory fixed firmly in the memory of mind and heart, each one of them labored to restore the vision to reality. The rampant ugly shrubs growing in the courtyards were torn up by their roots, and the seeds of flowers and fruit trees were planted. The stones of the building were cleansed of their sacrilegious markings. A new altar was built. And the scrolls, which had been rescued from the pillaging mercenaries of Antiochus by a priest, were returned to be placed on the new altar. One duty, alone, remained to be done.

Outside a chamber of the Temple called the Holy of Holies, a lamp was to be lighted. Until three years before a lamp had always guarded the Holy of Holies. Tended throughout the year by priests,

18

fueled with a specially prepared oil which only they were allowed to draw from sealed jars, this Eternal Light had blazed brightly and steadily from generation to generation, from the day of the Temple's first dedication unto the coming of Antiochus. It was the rekindling of this flame which would re-establish, finally and fully, exactly as before, the House of the God of Israel.

A priest was summoned to attend to the Eternal Light.

For three years this man had existed without performing the tasks which gave his life its meaning. He had lived in hiding, saving himself only for the day when he might serve his people again. Others might wonder whether there would be a people left to serve, but he was a priest and a pious man and he knew that his people would always survive.

With unwavering faith this priest had returned to the Temple. And now, with unfaltering steps, he made his way to the place where the oil was kept. For three years he had not visited this tiny chamber, and never before had he gone to it in near darkness. But until the Eternal Light was kindled there would, on this day, be no other fire within the Temple, and so there was only the gloom of a waning day to light his passage. Still, his steps did not falter as he made his way to get oil for the lamp.

In the tiny chamber he found, at first, only the jagged shards of broken containers. He was surprised. He knew he should not be— hadn't the Temple been despoiled in every other way?—but, just as he had never wondered at the source of his courage to go on believing in his God, he had never doubted that there would be fuel for the Eternal Light.

Probing with his hands through many scattered fragments of pottery, the priest finally felt the smooth, rounded surface of an unbroken jar. He pulled it from the debris and then went on looking for others. But there were none. From all the jars that had once been stored in this chamber, only one was left intact. Only this one. Enough oil for one night and one day. At sunset tomorrow, the flame of the Eternal Light would die. The Temple would be in darkness again.

The priest was dispirited by this thought. Had his people regained

19

the Temple only to fail in maintaining it? It would take at least a week to prepare more oil, or to bring more from another city to Jerusalem. In the meantime, were his people to worship without the symbols and traditions which they had fought for three years to preserve?

The priest knew that his people would not wait another day to rededicate the Temple. But what did it forbode to light the holy lamp, knowing that it could not be kept ablaze? Were the Jews to be driven so soon again from their sanctuary?

For a moment, an angry tempest of doubt swirled through the spirit of this priest. And then, like a hard bright shaft of sunlight piercing a stormcloud, something in his memory broke through and the doubt was suddenly gone.

He recalled that time, many years before, when Heliodorus, a minister of the Seleucid court, had come to Jerusalem with instructions from his king to empty the Temple treasury. The people whose goods were stored there for safekeeping protested, and the priests, whose trust it was to keep the faith of the people, pleaded with Heliodorus to abandon his mission. But he ignored these protests and pleas. And when the people turned at last to prayers, these too went unheard by Heliodorus. He came and entered the Temple even as many were still there praying that it would not be violated.

Onias, the High Priest, had met Heliodorus as he advanced upon the Temple steps accompanied by a guard of Seleucid mercenaries who would bear away the plunder. Once more Onias had attempted to repel these missionaries of Greed, but Heliodorus had passed by him and brought his guard to the portals of the treasury. Then, over the sound of many voices rising loud from the sanctuary, voices joined in prayer against him, Heliodorus had shouted his orders for the looting to begin.

Now there had occurred that event which shone in the priest's memory and reassured him.

As Heliodorus and his men went within the treasury, there appeared suddenly a sight both beautiful and terrible. A horse and rider came at them, charging fiercely. This horse, a beast of rare magnificence, seemed harnessed all in gold; and the rider also was

20

comely and clothed in beautiful apparel. And as this apparition bore down on them, Heliodorus and his men stood rooted with astonishment and terror. Then Heliodorus was felled—by the savage, flailing forefeet of the horse, it seemed—and two more young men appeared standing beside him. They scourged the fallen plunderer until his life began to ebb away through many wounds.

And, in the next second, the horse and rider and the two young men were gone.

The fearful attendants of Heliodorus had gathered up his almost lifeless body and begun to flee from the Temple. They were stopped by Onias. Seeing that the minister of the Seleucid king was near death, and afraid that the Jews might be punished for some treacherous attack, Onias had prayed for Heliodorus that he might recover his strength. Then life had flowed wondrously back into the crumpled shape of a man. And Heliodorus, perceiving the power of the God of the Temple, had offered sacrifice to this God and then gone away from Jerusalem.

This was the memory which reassured the priest. And bearing it in mind, he brought the one remaining jar of oil to the people and prepared to kindle the Eternal Light. Fearing for any sign that the Temple would be lost to them again, the people asked if it would be right to start the holy flame, knowing as they did that it could not be kept burning.

Now the priest reminded them of the story of Heliodorus, and thus were they reminded of the power of their God, and reassured that the Temple could truly embrace only that faith which did honor to Him. And sure in their hearts that they had returned to the Temple for all time, never to be cast out again, the people blended their voices together in joyous prayer and bade the priest to kindle the Eternal Light.

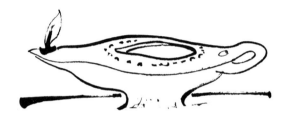

THE
SECOND
NIGHT

The sun had risen and traversed its arc over the city of Jerusalem. Only a narrow finger of light clung to the rim of distant hills, and soon this would slip away.

But still the holy flame burned bright and steady.

Throughout the preceding day and night throngs of worshippers had passed through the Temple. For three years each one of these Jews had carried an open wound in his spirit—a wound that refused to heal, a wound that could not be closed and scarred over by compromise and surrender. And now, in each one, the wound was suddenly healed by the sight of the Temple reclaimed and renewed. The flame of the Eternal Light, passing through their eyes, had entered into their spirits and burned away the infections of bitterness and hatred and doubt.

As the sun set, however, and the time approached when they knew that the Eternal Light would be exhausted of fuel, many in the Temple began to wrestle with new doubts. They were pious and trusting in their God—they had resisted hardship and suffering in order to remain true to Him—and yet they could not expel a suspicion that the Temple might soon again be taken from them. The story of Heliodorus no longer gave them comfort against their fears; it seemed to have happened in a dream, to have been told them in a dream. But their enemies were real. And the thought of the holy flame dwindling to darkness reminded them of these enemies—the tyrant who had once ordered the flame extinguished, and his armies, which were still in arms and sworn to vanquish the Jews. Might they not return—

23

perhaps tomorrow—and finally destroy the Temple, leveling it to the ground?

With this danger preying upon their minds, there were many who thought of leaving the Temple rather than see the Eternal Light fail before their eyes. They wanted to carry away a memory of the place as it looked fulfilled by its symbols, not as it looked in darkness.

But though many thought of leaving, none did. They could not bring themselves to sacrifice a single moment of the joy they felt in being able to worship once more in the Temple, instead of in dank cellars and mountain caves. They would not savor a moment less of this chance to honor God, knowing that tonight they would finish their prayers uninterrupted by those soldiers who in the past had punished their rituals with tortures and executions.

And so they remained in the Temple, their vague anxieties growing sharper as the sun disappeared and the night deepened, and the time came ever nearer when the Eternal Light would surely flicker out.

Through age-dimmed eyes, one old man watching the flame perceived only a vague tiny star at the center of a gray universe. Without this star, the old man's vision would be only of darkness. And yet, unlike most others, he was untroubled by an awareness that it might disappear. He gloried in the light while it lasted—and he was ready to accept a time when it would be there no more.

He had lived his life no differently, glorying in what God had given him—his body and mind and soul—and never fearing or resenting the time when they would be repossessed by the eternal. "The Lord giveth and the Lord taketh away." These words had given more than comfort to the old man; they had given him a weapon to fight the enemies of his faith. The threats of death they had spoken and whispered and shouted into his old ears could not make him abandon the Lord; for only if the Lord willed it could his life be taken. This was the old man's belief. And armed with nothing more, he had triumphed over kings.

So now, sensing the restlessness of those around him in the Temple, the old man spoke loud his belief: "The Lord giveth and the Lord

24

taketh away." And in an instant the restlessness was gone, and a listening silence filled the Temple. Then the old man went on, reminding the others that the flame might die, but the Lord would still be with them; in darkness or in light they need only be afraid if they lost faith.

The old man paused and listened. He could not see the faces around him as anything more than dim shapes; he could not see the look in any man's eyes—to know what had been the effect of his words. So the old man listened. And it seemed to him that all around him were holding their breath, as if waiting for something more. Something to make the words they had heard many times in the past come alive to them in some new way.

And so the old man told them the story of Eleazar:

He had long been living in Jerusalem when Antiochus came. The tyrant entered the city in wrath, having come to repress a jubilant uprising occasioned by rumors of his own death in battle with the Egyptians. To revenge himself upon the people who so vividly despised him, Antiochus had taken his legions through the streets— the same streets where the people had been celebrating—plundering and killing and taking the Jews for slaves. When Antiochus had gone away, he had left the city awash with blood, reeking of rotting flesh, filled with the screams of the wounded and the mourning. The aftermath of massacre assaulted the senses of every survivor.

And it crippled their spirit. Many who had been pious until now lost faith in the God who would allow such calamity to befall them. Others gave themselves up to the Lord overzealously, praying for His own hand to reach into their lives, touch their shoulders and awaken them from this nightmare reality. And they also were disappointed and so turned away from God.

Even those who demanded no miracles, whose prayers for salvation were offered with humility and traditional dignity—even their faith was threatened in the wake of Antiochus' vengeance. For he had left behind his own governor over Judea, and new harsh measures were taken against the Jews. Special taxes were levied against them. Curfews were imposed. Soldiers were encouraged to harass their worship, and ridicule the customs of their daily living. Moreover, the li-

25

centious Dionysian spectacles of the Hellenists were paraded before the Jews, and many of their youth were drawn in and permanently corrupted. By all these means did Antiochus continue to cut down their number, even after he had sheathed his sword and marched away to humble other peoples.

And yet, there were some whose faith remained unshakable, who found in it their sword and their shield and their sustenance. Daily they went to the Temple—which Antiochus had not yet taken from them—and said, in these times of hardship, the same prayers they had said in times of joy. Prayers to honor God.

Among them, no voice could be heard to intone the ancient words more firmly than that of Eleazar. So strong and sure was his belief that many around him who would otherwise have despaired were inspired. When Eleazer made his way to the Temple, many who would have stood and watched others go by followed him, knowing that when he turned his clear proud gaze in answer to the jeers of nonbelievers, they would draw back and let Eleazar pass unmolested.

The effect of this pious old man, and others like him, on the Jews of Jerusalem did not fail to attract the notice of the governor Antiochus had left over them. He knew that if he were to please the king by suppressing the Jews into extinction, he would have to eliminate the men from whom they drew inspiration. The high priests of the Temple were no longer a problem. They had begun intriguing to catch the favor of the king, and the people no longer trusted them. But there were still men like Eleazar. And how could they be dealt with? If they were summarily killed or imprisoned, the governor feared, their martyrdom might stir the Jews to rebellion. Therefore, although he knew they were a danger, the governor did not harm them. He bided his time, and hoped for their hearts to give out by themselves—hoped that they would die, or succumb to the pressures of ridicule or bribery.

And some did. But those, like Eleazar, who survived, continued to draw their people around them and give them courage. And with the passing of two years, the spirit of the Jews had recovered from the slaughter that Antiochus had wrought in their midst, and they began to strain against his oppression.

The tyrant was now back in Egypt, engaged in new wars. Messengers were sent to him, warning of the Jews' growing determination to be free, and he vowed to answer with an army which would destroy the Jews for all time to come. Unable to lead this army himself, he sent one of his generals, Apollonius.

When the legions of Apollonius came to Jerusalem they made no initial show of hostility. This surprised the Jews, who expected only treachery and violence to spring from any mission of Antiochus. But after several days had passed, and the soldiers had been in the city without any of them going amongst the people, the Jews' wariness subsided. And with the coming of the Sabbath, they thanked God that no new calamity had befallen them.

Then it was that Apollonius struck. He had waited for the Sabbath, knowing that the Jews' religion forbade them to bear arms on that day; therefore might his mission to liquidate them be accomplished more easily and more thoroughly.

The killing went on through the day and into the night. When the sun had set and the Jews were at last able to pick up their weapons without committing a sacrilege, there were too few of the young and the strong left alive to offer any great resistance. The people stood helplessly as their houses were pulled down, the walls of their city demolished, their Temple sacked and defiled, and the blood let from their bodies into the streets.

This easy murder would have continued into other days and nights had not the soldiers of Apollonius finally turned away from their hideous task. The endless, wanton hacking at human flesh had made them all weary and sick and disgusted with their mission. And so the massacre ended.

But some Jews had survived. And Apollonius, who was now governor over Judea, sought for other means to deal with them. Seeing that his soldiers were surfeited with senseless killing, he established laws which gave the killing reason. Any Jew found worshipping his God, or following the ancient customs of his faith, was to be executed. Thus did Apollonius, by having his soldiers uphold his law, give them reason to kill any Jew who remained a Jew.

Still the people of Israel endured; men lived who could not be shaken from their faith. And among them was Eleazar. Nightly he read from the Torah, just as he had done in the Temple; and each week he kept the Sabbath. Although both of these deeds were punishable by death, many joined Eleazar in keeping the faith when they saw the old man's courage. And so the faith was kept alive.

Now Apollonius realized that if he could make men like Eleazar abandon Judaism, he would have found the most effective means of subverting the mass of Jews. Just as these men led their people in piety, they might be made to lead them in conversion. Therefore, Apollonius dispatched soldiers to find the most pious elders and humble them before their own people, forcing them to accept Hellenistic ways.

For this purpose, a troop of the governor's men came at last to the house of Eleazar. With them they carried an altar adorned with idols. This they set down before the door of the house; and then they ordered Eleazar to come forth.

The old man appeared. He knew why the soldiers had come, but there was no hint of apprehension about him—in his eyes or in the way he stood. He looked with hard disdain upon the idol, and stood unbowed, uncringing as the soldiers advanced, with drawn swords, to seize him and bring him to his knees.

A crowd of his people saw Eleazar brought to his knees. But they saw, too, that he could not be made to say the words of obeisance demanded by the soldiers. And in this, they took heart. They grieved for Eleazar's suffering, but they rejoiced in the strength he was receiving from God.

The danger of Eleazar's example was not lost upon the soldiers. They resolved even more firmly to show the people that the old man's will could be broken. If words against his religion could not be brought up out of his throat, then they would put something down it to the same purpose. The meat of swine was brought and pressed to Eleazar's lips. But against all the efforts the soldiers made to open his mouth—the pressure of their crude hands, and the pain they inflicted with their swords—Eleazar set his jaw tightly. And they were unable to make him partake of the unclean meat.

Seeing this, the crowd around Eleazar surged forward to save him, but the soldiers turned their swords upon them and drove them back. They were afraid now, however—the soldiers—not of the angry crowd, but of the old man's indomitable spirit. If it could not be broken, it seemed to foretell of their own eventual destruction. And so they were determined to have him vow allegiance to their Hellenist gods.

They brought his possessions before him and swore to destroy them all, unless he knelt at their altar and said their prayers. But he would not. He watched his house brought to ruins, and his meager crops burned, and his animals slain. But Eleazar would give homage to none but his God.

At length even the soldiers stood in awe of the old man, who remained unyielding amidst the wreckage of all he had owned. And they felt, desperately, that if they could not make him forswear his beliefs, they would have suffered an ominous defeat. But what could they do to him now? Only kill him. And he would die with all his convictions intact, before a crowd of his people.

Then one of the soldiers conceived a way around the old man's resolution. He brought to Eleazar a piece of meat, cut from an animal which the Jews did not consider unclean. If the old man would eat of this, allowing those who watched to believe that it had come from swine, the soldier promised to leave him in peace.

Eleazar smiled at this. In peace? He knew he would have no peace while he lived if he allowed this deception. The soldier saw the quick smile and perceived Eleazar's thought. Bringing his dagger up to the old man's throat, he urged him once more, whispering to him sharply, fearfully: "We are not asking you to violate your religion; this is not pig's meat."

Could they understand so little of his religion, Eleazar wondered. He shook his head in bemusement—and in refusal of the soldier's final offer. In the next instant, he was dead.

The storyteller said no more of Eleazar. But his words lingered in the air as all in the Temple waited for the Eternal Light to burn out. Now they were no longer afraid, for they realized a religion which lived apart from the symbol; they sensed a temple, beyond the structure of stone on stone, which could never be destroyed. It was not just a diet they believed in, or a flame; it was a way of living—freely, with dignity and with truth.

This was what the Lord gave them, and what was taken away from those who lost faith.

Mindful of this, the people began to pray. And not for a long time did they realize that the light, which was supposed to die, had continued to burn through the night.

THE THIRD NIGHT

How many thousand eyes shone from the darkness with the reflected image of that constant flame. Crowded together on crude wooden benches, crouched on the Temple's cold stone floor, gathered along the walls and in the farthest corners of the vast sanctuary, the Jews of Jerusalem watched and waited. And more waited outside, beyond the open doors, and in the great courtyard beyond that; and others stood even farther back, where the tapering arm of lamplight spent its last strength to flick away heavy shadows and hold off the moonless night.

The sound of prayer rose from the watchful mass—this sound and no other, no words but holy words. They did not ask among themselves what bound them to their vigil; there were things, they all realized, that could not be known. But still they wondered in silence: what force held them in thrall before a pinpoint of light? What made them all think, at times, that within this flame they could see, looking back at them, an infinite eye? It had burned for two days— one day beyond the time they had thought allowed by nature—and they had been thus reassured. But nature constantly arranged larger surprises, and offered greater reassurance, and crowds did not gather. Grapes appeared on a vine, corn pushed through the ground, leaves turned from green to gold, oceans crept up across the sand and then retreated, the sun climbed into the sky, descended, and then rose again—day after day, season after season—and crowds did not gather. Yet here, now, because less than a handful of fire had lingered too long, a multitude stood transfixed. Why? To witness a miracle? Who among them believed that a miracle could be so small? . . .

33

Separated from the crowd, beneath a fig tree in the most distant reaches of the courtyard one man looked on, his mind as uncluttered by question as his eyes were clouded by a mist of regret.

Like a wanderer in a wasteland come upon a single flower, like a child of famine nourished on ashes, tasting at last a single drop of honey on his tongue, this man had been prepared by circumstance to find magnificence in the simplest moment. For he had not in many years stood with his people at prayer, nor seen the sacred parchments carried in procession, nor heard the recitation of psalms. Nor had he, until this night, felt the absence of these quiet glories.

But now he did. Tonight, drawn back mysteriously to the Temple by streets which whispered of an unfinished phenomenon, he had come upon a long sought after revelation. Suddenly he was free of the uncertainties which had gnawed sharply, relentlessly—like small vicious animals living in his mind—at his faith. And as if he were a world unto himself, a planet formed out of the sun and given life by its power, he was born again as a Jew in the presence of the flame.

He had been one of the "letzim"—a Hellenist Jew—and so he was, perhaps always would be, an outcast. For a thousand endless days and restless nights he had suffered the hatred and scorn of his brothers. He had borne the stigma without shame, however, for he had not turned to other gods out of weakness or fear. He had not, like most of the letzim, been driven by pain or hunger to pay dishonest homages. His visits to strange pillared places of worship, and the demands his heart had made before strange deities, were prompted by no different desire than that which had brought him once to the Temple and to its priests: the desire of all men under the stars for peace and truth.

It had seemed to him, in the days when he had turned from his ancient religion to embrace Hellenism, that truth no longer went forth from the House of Israel, and that peace could not be found there. For the priests themselves were engaged in intrigues and treacheries to rival those of the Jews' most hated enemies; more than one High Priest had found the way to his place of honor through

34

infamy. And because this man had once been a faithful follower of Jehovah, and so constantly in the presence of the priests, he too had felt enmeshed in their evil.

Not since Onias had a High Priest worn creditably the white robes and golden trappings of the Temple's most sacred estate. Indeed, ironically, it was his righteousness—and the power which God had delivered into his hands because of it—which seemed, indirectly, to have destroyed Onias and led to the ascension of his despicable successors.

Heliodorus, whom Onias, invoking God's help, had brought down in defense of the Temple treasury, had then been spared to return in good health to his king. This was the Syrian tyrant, Seleucus Philopater, who had issued to Heliodorus a specific charge to bring back gold from Jerusalem. Without this new wealth, Seleucus feared he might not be able to dispense his Roman tribute, and he was furious to learn that Heliodorus had failed so ignominiously in his mission. Had an armed guard not entered with him into the Temple? How could the force of men and arms be driven out by a vision? No explanation by Heliodorus could dissolve the king's doubt, or counter his ridicule. And the feud which finally resulted had lasted several months, ending only when Heliodorus poisoned the king and usurped his title.

But the poisoner's peace had been short-lived. Hearing of Seleucus' death while warring in Egypt, his brother soon made his way back to Syria and, with the help of another king, crushed the rebellion. Thus unfolded the events which had brought Antiochus IV—destined to be the Jews' most terrifying enemy—to the Seleucid throne.

It was the custom of the Empire for each of its parts to send emissaries of good will to a new king. In the letter of that custom—but not in the spirit, for there was no good will in Judea toward the Seleucids—Onias had selected his brother Joshua as missionary to the court of Antiochus. And now occurred the first of those perfidies which had debased the priesthood.

Shunning that same heritage which he was charged to represent, Joshua had come before Antiochus calling himself by the Greek name Jason. So doing, he had implied his sympathy with the king's

35

desire to undermine and eventually eliminate the Jewish tradition. And when, furthermore, Jason had promised to increase the amount of tribute paid to Antiochus from Jerusalem, the king had readily agreed to depose Onias and abet the ambitions of his brother. Then had Jason returned unto the realms of his people, accompanied by a contingent of the king's soldiers, and forcibly assumed the prerogatives and sacred duties of God's agent on earth.

But to the Lord Himself, Jason showed no greater allegiance than he had to his own brother. He wielded power over his congregation not to encourage their piety and ward off the menace to their continuity, but conversely to weaken their will and blur their purpose. Schools were established to educate the youth in the Greek manner; Talmudic scholarship—the concentrated study of Hebrew law and language—was discouraged or abandoned, and in its place were taught the impious propositions of such contrasting philosophies as Stoicism and Hedonism. Moreover, Jason ordered a stadium to be constructed where the youth of Jerusalem might test themselves, one against another, brother pitted against brother—as Jason had pitted himself against Onias—in Greek athletic combat.

True, not all of these things might be deemed inherently evil: there were, the Jews acknowledged, admirable lessons to be learned in some Greek philosophy—elements of ideology which coincided with the most ancient Hebrew teachings; and there were benefits to be had too from giving young men a chance to develop their minds and bodies in athletic contests. But if there were these positive aspects to Jason's design, he did not stress them. And the elders of the Jewish community came to perceive that Jason's basic intent was to divide them from their children and so, by robbing the Temple of its vitality, make his word absolute. Without such incontestable power Jason had caused to fear the future; he had recognized as inevitable a time when, to meet the terms by which Antiochus had raised him to authority, he would have to plunder the very place which his brother had once in the past successfully petitioned God to protect.

As it happened, the lesser priest whom Jason had dispatched to Antiochus with the third of his annual tributes delivered as well a

36

promise of his own for greater revenues. Thus had Jason's holy office been taken from him and passed into the hands of Menelaus.

These were the machinations which had preceded the terrible event remembered by one man who stood this night alone beneath a fig tree in a far reach of the Temple court, gazing at a luminous yellow spot set like a jewel into the distant air.

He had not yet sought his place among the letzim when Menelaus became High Priest. Although confused by the stories he had heard of unscrupulous actions taken by one priest against another, he had been able to continue his worship at the Temple exactly as in the time of Onias, and therefore he had not felt the need for any involvement, any protest, on his own part. His prayers were uttered, the rituals observed daily as of old; and he was content that, whatever might be said of other men, he was a good Jew.

But forces had been set in motion which were to shake his convictions, violently, and send him on a desperate odyssey for new truths.

Just as Jason had known he would have to sell the Temple gold to meet his obligations to Antiochus, it was now clear that Menelaus had assumed the same ignoble responsibility. Recognizing an opportunity to discredit Menelaus and ultimately return himself to power, Jason brought word to Onias that the treasury was to be looted.

Then Onias went forth to guarantee, as he had once before, the inviolability of the Temple and its resources. But this time no vision appeared to help him. And when Onias warned Lysimachus—the corrupt brother of Menelaus into whose hands the treasury had been entrusted—that he would raise every Jew in arms against these infamous priests sooner than let them strip the splendor from the House of God, he had been fatally struck down.

From under a fig tree, through massive doors swung wide, one man stared deep into a place which, but for a tiny eye of fire, would be only blackness. And he heard out of his memory the chorus of angry staccato sounds which had come to his ears when, on a day long ago, he had sat there in prayer. He saw again the tangled gathering of shadows which had loomed on the high walls—evil spirits loosed by man's vengeance—and felt the heat of fury, and smelled

37

the pungent odor of blood lust. And with every sense he sat once more to witness Lysimachus driven back by a mob into the treasury and there killed—murdered to avenge the death of Onias, whose goodness the people had never failed to regard with esteem.

He had gone out of the Temple that day without a God. Or so he believed. And who was there to argue with his answers to these questions: Can these priests have served anything but themselves? Can there be a God if those nearest to Him can do such evil? Can there be goodness at all if, in its name, mobs can kill?

Yet after many days a time had come when he looked into the sky and wondered anew who had hung the stars and fixed the earth at their center. But he did not turn back to the Temple for his answer. He found that he could believe more easily in many gods, rather than one God. He found that a god of the sun, a god of the soil, a god of the sea, goddesses of the moon, the hunt, the harvest—each ruled

over something tangible, something which could be watched and understood. The Greeks claimed no god of the soul; their gods did not accept responsibility for the quality of human deeds.

And so, thinking himself no longer in danger of disenchantment, he worshipped among the Greeks—although he continued to live among the Jews. He was loathed and denounced by his neighbors, but this seemed a necessary ordeal standing between him and some final contentment. If there were any doubts remaining about the desertion from his father's faith, they were quelled when he saw new intrigues among the priests. Supported by the king's garrison, Menelaus had remained High Priest even after the murder of Lysimachus; then, when rumors had come to Jerusalem of Antiochus' death in Egypt, Jason had again seized away the sacred power.

It was then that Antiochus had appeared alive, alive with sword flailing before him, alive to order the slaughter of others. It was then that he had begun to force new gods upon all the Jews, to make laws and issue proclamations forbidding worship of any deities but those of the pantheon. And when these measures had failed, it was then that he had wrought more death and destruction, and finally defiled the Temple.

So where had his search brought him—this man who had gone among the letzim? Could he accept divinities upheld by blood-soaked soldiers any more than a God attended by criminally scheming priests? His spirit foundered, hopeless. And looking on through the next few years at the struggle which raged in Judea—that struggle which sent a band of men called the Maccabees into the wilderness—he saw not a test of religions or a quarrel of gods, but only the pitiful folly of men. Godless men, like himself.

But were these men godless who stood everywhere around him tonight in the courtyard of the Temple they had fought to reclaim? In the lamplight, their shadows blending, falling across each other noiselessly, sharing the same ground, he saw them as something more than the servants of their own lusts and hungers. They had challenged a tyrant to preserve something beyond themselves—and now their effort had been acknowledged. Not alone by the return of the Temple. By the flame which remained alive within it.

It was the flame, he realized now, and even more the trust of those who gathered to watch it, which made the Temple a holy place. And it would exist eternally as such whatever the temper of its priests. He had been wrong to think that their infamies proved the absence of his ancient God, and wrong to think that they were truer gods who let his spirit rest without self-questioning: only by questioning his actions and those of other men in the light of truths beyond his own existence could he achieve the good which God intended.

These were the realizations which occurred to this Jew reborn before the flame. And looking into it he felt a surge of boundless hope, like a tide rising under a brilliant moon.

THE
FOURTH
NIGHT

In the eyes of a boy, the Temple had been revealed as a palace. There was no throne in its inner chamber, no vain decoration on its walls, the people who came through its gates were dressed plainly and not in robes of silk and gold, and yet it was the most splendid dwelling of any king. The flame which burned in its great hall, he was sure, had been kindled by the same hand which lit the torches of Heaven, and its towers reached up beyond the sun. It was certainly, the boy thought, the one true palace on earth—the only indestructible citadel of the only true King.

He had been taken once, many days before, into the presence of a man who was called "king." And he had seen this man surrounded by all the proud appurtenances of power. The king had been seated high above the heads of all other men, his jewel-heavy fingers curled around the arms of a massive ebony throne. At his feet every precious substance of the world was lain to buy his favor. Soldiers and ministers in glorious raiment were ready to fulfill his every command. This was the tyrant who had—perhaps with no more than a whispered word—ordered a whole people to extinction.

The boy was one of these people—a Jew. He had been taken out of his home in Judea and brought, in a caravan along with many others like him, all the way to Antioch. At the city they had all been left for many days crowded unbearably into dank, stinking dungeons. The boy remembered a flood of hot dark hours spilling over his senses until time had become meaningless; each minute was the same minute, each day was all days. And then suddenly he had been wrenched out

43

of this torpid, numbing nothingness and led through a maze of cavernous passages to emerge into a blinding opulence. The glitter of gems and gold had chiseled painfully through the crust of indifference which had formed over his brain. And when it had been shattered completely, he believed that he had risen up not to a mere mortal domain, but to some divine precinct.

There were others like the boy who had been brought to the palace of Antiochus. But they had understood better than he what was the true nature of this dazzling place, and of its master. For, unlike him, they were not alone and without the counsel of their elders.

His mother and father had been killed by the Macedonian soldiers who had come to take them away. They had heard of the caravans which took their people to Antioch, and they had vowed never to let themselves or their children be put to the cruel tests which Antiochus was said to inflict on pious Jews. But there had been no warning, no chance to flee. There had only been time to hide the boy and his brothers, before the soldiers had burst into their home. Then, true to their vow, the man and his wife had flailed fiercely at their abductors, knowing it would mean their own deaths. Afterward, the house had been looted, and the children had been found under a thin pile of animal skins. Somewhere—the boy could not remember exactly how—the brothers had been separated; he had simply awakened and reached out and found them gone.

So he knew that murder had been done to bring him to Antioch; he knew that he had been tried there in darkness and stench, alone. And yet the splendor of the place into which he had emerged from his suffering seemed fit only for the habitation of a god. He was still young enough to be confused by this, still innocent enough to find an unacceptable paradox in seeing wealth and power as the property of evil. And when he had come finally into the presence of the king, he had waited expectantly to witness some ultimate good.

He had seen instead only a succession of the most terrible inhuman deeds.

Antiochus had not been able to comprehend the resistance raised by the Jews against his decrees. How was it possible for any of them to hope for victory, much less survival, in the face of his might? And

44

why were they so ready to die rather than say a few words in praise of the god who bridled the sun, or the goddess who tended the moon? Why had they always preferred to be cut down rather than to permit the flesh of certain tame animals to be brought to their lips?

Once these questions had seemed almost trivial to Antiochus, part of a game that all kings played. Only in idle moments had he attempted to puzzle out the futile endeavors of small men—men without power—to arrange their own fate. Fate, he had been sure, was the sovereign territory of kings; the one invisible nation which they ruled together as allies.

But time had passed and his messengers had begun to bring tales from Judea of a particular group of Jews gathering force in the mountains above the Jordan Valley. And for some reason, as he heard more and more frequently about these people, the edge on the king's teasing speculations about the Jews became sharper and sharper, until, at last, they no longer tickled his conceit, but grated on it and made it raw.

Then Antiochus had become obsessed by a desire to prove that the Jews' resistance was a puny, hopeless gesture. And he had issued an order for his soldiers to bring captive Jews to the great city from which he commanded his empire. There, in his palace, he would tear the piety out of their souls until all of them, everywhere, realized the folly of sustaining their peculiar religious zeal and submitted meekly to his gods.

In this way had the boy from Judea arrived with a hundred others —and trailing the ghosts of many thousands more—to be tested against the king's obsession. But even before his own turn had come, he had seen the triumph of simple faith over tyranny which had revealed the limits of earthly power and the hollow illusion of earthly palaces.

Among the captives who had been brought, along with the boy, before Antiochus, there had been a fatherless family of eight—a mother and her seven sons. The boy had noticed them immediately when they had been herded into the throne room. The seven young men had stood erect and seemingly unafraid, surrounding their mother. Her hands had not been laid gently upon any of them, her arms had not sheltered even the smallest in a protective embrace, and her

45

eyes had never sought theirs reassuringly. But in the way her eyes had burned fixedly across the span of great distance which separated her from the platform where the king sat swathed in comfort, it was clear that a holy fury raged within her. And, to the boy, it had looked as if the strength of her conviction flowed into her sons, like blood pumping from her heart into their veins. The sight of this woman had been an inspiration for the boy, too; and he had felt, in merely looking at her, that in some strange way he was also her son.

And when the boy saw the moment approaching when the woman and her seven sons would be summoned to walk down the far expanse which led to the feet of the king, he began to tremble in awe of the terrible imminent clash. His naive expectation of ultimate justice had been dispelled as he watched the king making his brutal assault on the spirit of the Jews. Antiochus, he knew now, was capable only of unmitigated evil, in ever worsening proportion.

Horrified, the boy had observed as his people, one after another, had been commanded to eat the meat of swine and make pagan libations—and had been slain for their refusal. The deaths of the first few had been swift; "merciful" could have described even these cold-blooded murders in comparison to the atrocities that were to follow. For as Antiochus was thwarted again and again, his rage grew and he began to inflict unspeakable tortures on these proud and pious Jews, cutting and maiming them with sword and fire before they were allowed to release those last pleading sighs which would echo into eternity.

Faced with the prospect of these agonizing ordeals, some Jews began to retreat, to surrender to the king's monstrous resolution. And when the tyrant saw them giving way, he was in part appeased. But he also knew that the most severe measures had brought him his only tangible successes against the Jews. And he continued to apply the most excruciating tortures against those that resisted him.

Thus, when the woman named Hannah and her seven sons came in their turn before Antiochus, he was prepared to do his worst should they defy his will. This fact was apparent to all the Jews who remained alive, awaiting their own judgment there in the throne room. And they froze tensely as the king called to the first boy and ordered him to go to the large copper pan where the meat of pigs was being fried in its own fat, and to eat of it unsparingly.

The boy did not move from beside his mother. He looked up wonderingly at Antiochus, and in a gentle voice—a voice which seemed somehow to function as the instrument for expressing the words which spoke silently from the eyes of his mother—the boy said to the king: "What wouldst thou ask or learn of us? We are ready to die rather than to transgress the laws of our fathers."

Hearing this, the king erupted into a singular fury, and he instructed his soldiers to seize the boy and place him bodily into that same copper pan where the forbidden meat was being seared and charred. And there, in the sight of his closest kin, the first boy perished.

Now Antiochus demanded of another of Hannah's children that he eat from the pan. But as the command had been made doubly repellent, this boy answered the king like the first, and the soldiers set upon him, too, to cut out his tongue, to scourge him with hot irons, and lash him until life had become a stranger to his ruined body.

Still, when the third boy was called, he did not cower in the shadow of the king, nor did he shrink from declaring his everlasting faith in his ancient God. And for him, Antiochus bid the soldiers to conceive even worse punishment, and he suffered all the torments of his dead brothers and more.

Unnerved by the sure courage with which these three young Jews had accepted death sooner than shun their tradition, Antiochus paused from his headlong slaughter to rail against the folly of their actions. Why did they insist on perishing, when he asked so little of them as the price for their lives?

To this question, the boys did not reply. But their mother spoke, not in answer to the king, but to pacify even the smallest doubt which might trouble any of her surviving children:

"I cannot tell you how came ye into my womb; for I neither gave you breath nor life, neither was it I that formed the members of every one of you; but doubtless the Creator of the world, who formed the generation of man, and found out the beginning of all things, will also of His own mercy give you breath and life again, as ye now regard not your own selves for His laws' sake."

Her words angered the king more dreadfully than before; and when the next three of Hannah's sons refused to pay homage at his altar, he made them to suffer the fiercest pains of all, ordering his soldiers to cut off all the appendages of their bodies, and then to punish them beyond that until they died of their wounds.

Now there remained only one of Hannah's seven sons alive on earth. And, seeing that the most horrendous afflictions had not caused the brothers of this one to swerve from their righteous path, Antiochus swore inwardly to win him without threats. The proud king promised his young prisoner a share in all the wealth of his empire, if the boy would only forsake the God of Israel. Antiochus was sincere in this promise, for he had marveled at the courage displayed by all this family, and he knew that it would be well to have one of them raised up in his court, perhaps someday to serve as one of his generals.

But as his brothers had spoken softly in reply to the king's furious ravings, so fiercely did the last boy speak in refusing the king's seductive lure. And he called down the wrath of Almighty God upon Antiochus and his house, and all the tyrants who would come after him, to his house or any other.

The king shouted frantically to drown out this fearful invocation, and called his soldiers immediately against the boy to destroy him. Then he sentenced his mother to die, the woman who had brought him and all his brothers into this world, and delivered them out of it by her prayers. So, at last, the family was extinguished.

But already, on that day, their tranquil battle had sapped the vital energy of the king. He appeared suddenly discouraged and fearful of persisting in his persecution. And in a strange, languorous voice —a voice that seemed somehow to be other than his own—he commanded the guards to free all the captive Jews who were still there alive in his presence.

He had been one of the fortunate few—this boy who sat in the Temple tonight watching the miraculous flame. And just as he observed it to live on by the power of God, long beyond the term or reason understood by men, he knew that Hannah and her seven sons lived on, too.

As a son and a brother—as all in the Temple were Hannah's children, and her children's kin—the boy blessed their memory. They who had instructed him in the secrets of power; they who had taught him to perceive that on this night, as never before, he had truly come into a palace.

THE
FIFTH
NIGHT

There were some who had begun to wonder, on the fourth day after the kindling of the lamp, whether it might not continue to burn for the rest of time. If this were the Lord's design, they said, then surely a mass vigil could not always be kept before the flame. A time would come—perhaps had come already—when the people must understand the miracle to be a part of their existence, and return to living a portion of their days away from the Temple.

The suggestion had seemed blasphemous. Could the terms of a miracle be pronounced by men? The Lord's intentions were known only to Him, and they might be fathomed only according to the signs He made. By His power He had returned the people to the Temple, by a wonder He had shown them His presence; now they would not go out from the Temple until He showed that to be His will. This was the mind of the people, and so those few who thought differently were silenced.

And yet, when the fifth day came and the light still gleamed, the voices of these few silent men could again be heard. Their unwanted words had taken hold in the minds of the people, and everyone asked within himself if indeed the light might be extinguished only after the last star. To imagine the Temple without its special luminosity was certainly to imagine a different, a less magnificent place. A place somehow farther removed from the dominions of God. And would He estrange those that He had now brought so near to Him? Having woven a dream, would He unravel a single thread?

Although they would not speak of it to each other, now all in the

51

Temple began to think of a time when they would go away—away to their homes and fields, away to the lives of work and love which had been ruined for them by Antiochus, or which they had given up to fight him—leaving the flame alive behind them as an assurance that God would protect them ever after.

She thought of walking along the winding cart track that led out from Jerusalem toward the sea and, after a half day's walk, to the gently rising hills above her home. In her memory she saw the town

as she had seen it on many evenings, when she had looked down from the hill which she had climbed to call her husband in from his vineyard: a few rows of small square, white clay houses surrounding a large open space of dusty trampled earth. This clearing at the town's center was the meeting place, the market place, the place where she had gone every day under a high sun to draw water from a well and talk happily with other women of the town, the place where men exchanged proud boasts of the harvest each had reaped in his fields, and laughed over the misadventures of their growing sons. It was also

the place where she had seen a few men rise in anger against many, and begin the struggle which had brought her and many others far from their homes, through bloody battles, to the sanctuary of the Temple. For the town which filled her memory was Modin—the birthplace of the Maccabees.

But their battles were over now, and they had won, and she tried to forget the days of torment, of cold and wilderness, of chaos and blood, and think only of the town as a place to return for peace and warmth. Her memory led her along the cart track, down out of the hills, and across one of the fields which ringed the small cluster of clay houses. And she walked unmoving through orchards of apple and fig trees, through caressing wisps of high wheat, through patches of barley and corn, and groves of orange and lemon trees, through gardens of cabbage, turnip, cucumber, and melon, into the streets of Modin.

Remembered sounds rose in her ears. The cries of children, the bleating of goats and sheep, and the cackling of hens mingled with a vision of the passageways between sun-bleached walls. Colors and smells stirred her senses as she walked on in memory—close-by doorways wreathed with honeysuckle and roses in spring and summer, where strings of dried fruit hung heavily on autumn days.

And then her thoughts came to the open ground at the center of Modin. Again she tried to think of it as it would be after she and others returned to inhabit their long-empty homes, a place for talk and laughter, arrayed with fruit and flowers, and jugs of new wine. But although in her mind an image clung of her people assembled there, she did not see them gathered in friendship or celebration, but for a grim encounter with dark forces.

In the time of Alexander the Great, when Judea had been absorbed into the Macedonian Empire, its people had been allowed to continue living according to their own ancient traditions. The governor whom Alexander had placed over them before marching away to other conquests was chosen from among them; and throughout the land each small village—like Modin—was permitted to plot the simple destiny of its days exactly as in centuries past. Then, when Alexander had died and his empire had been divided among three of his generals, they had attempted to consolidate their separate powers by unifying the hierarchy and custom of each of their realms. Macedonian deputies were placed in authority over groups of villages, and they went frequently into the towns to collect large taxes and to promote, by bribery, cajolery and coercion, the replacement of all Hebraic practices by Hellenism.

She had heard her elders in Modin speak of the untroubled life which the Jews had led in the days of Alexander. This had been almost two hundred years earlier, but such was the nostalgia of the Jews for a time when they had known freedom to follow the dictates of their hearts, that each generation tried to believe that it had known this freedom. The "remembrance" of its sweetness was spoken of often, and so had passed down through several lifetimes. Hearing constantly of this nostalgic dream, she, like all the other people of Modin, had longed deeply to be free. And from her longing she had found a will to resist the invasion of her spirit, despite even the cruelest oppression which had come after the accession of Antiochus.

But it was not only an intense wish which had kept the people of Modin strong against hardship, unfailing in their beliefs. Other people in other towns harbored the same wish—but this alone had not been enough to prevent their easy surrender when the Seleucid warden, accompanied by Macedonian soldiers, had passed through their streets demanding the destruction of their ceremonial treasures and forcing them into mass sacrifices to alien gods. The warden had brought his troops into Modin, too. But each time he had been confronted by a man whose quiet, certain refusal to permit the sacrifice had strangely unsettled the warden and caused him to lead the soldiers away without enforcing his demands.

This man's name was Mattathias. He was the Adon of Modin—the rabbi, the interpreter of the holy law by which the people ordered every action of their lives. The power he held traditionally was no different from that of other rabbis in many other towns. But this was not the power which encouraged the people of Modin to stand behind him unafraid when he faced the Seleucid emissaries and scorned their commands. Something in his posture, in the way his words boldly split the air, in the way he looked at his enemies, his eyes sparking like flint striking rock, suggested that he had a great ally against those enemies—that his mandate to determine events had not been bestowed by men alone. And this had been sensed not only by his own people, who needed his inspiration, but by those who damned him for it.

Yet, would the Seleucids always retreat from this man? By the sword they held half a world in submission. Balanced on a sharp steel edge, they ruled over a score of lands, over millions who despised their rule. If there were anything to fear from a man who bore no arms, who carried no shield, then they could fear for an empire. The steel must be proven, the edge constantly sharpened, against every insurgent. They could allow neither their subjects nor themselves to suspect the source of their supremacy.

In the Temple, standing as one of a multitude before a flame, she stood in memory on a space of dusty ground in Modin among a crowd of her neighbors. On that day, too, all eyes had focused on a single sign of hope.

A new Seleucid official had been appointed to enforce the edicts of Antiochus. He had come to Modin clearly determined to see the Jews humbled before the altar of Apollo—or see them dead. This warden, Apelles, had brought a complement of eighty soldiers, and ten slaves who carried a blood-darkened stone to which was affixed a graven idol of the sun god.

But Mattathias had met the challenge of Apelles with no less determination than he had mustered against all the other Seleucid efforts to pervert his religion. Even before Apelles had brought his troop of mercenaries into the center of town, Mattathias had summoned the people of Modin to meet there. And he had arranged them as they would be to greet the disrupter of their peace: standing close together with himself at their head a few paces in front, flanked by his sons.

They had been only his sons then, she thought. Jochanan, Simon, Jonathan, Eleazar and Judah. In her memory of the moment they were merely young men reflecting a descendancy of strength from their father, not yet having shown their own heroic tempers. It would

56

be a while before all of them, the father and the sons, came to be called the Maccabees—"the hammerers."

When the altar was set down and the soldiers had formed around it with drawn swords, Mattathias alone had stepped forward. Only his shadow had skimmed like a spear across the ground before Apelles; only his voice had risen into the breeze to rival the ominous music of clattering armor. The children who had earlier been playing noisily at games stood next to their mothers, huddled soundless in the folds of their raw linen cloaks. The bleating animals had fled off the streets into a hundred hidden darknesses after one of the soldiers had stunned a goat and dragged it to the altar. In the still afternoon the Adon's declaration rang out like a hammer smiting an anvil, forging truth out of silence. Never, he vowed, would he allow any Jew of Modin to commit a sacrilege against the Lord Jehovah.

Apelles had warned Mattathias that all those who shunned Apollo's altar would be put to death. But without hesitation the Adon delivered his doom-bound oath; and in the faces of the few hundred people clustered behind their rabbi, Apelles could detect no sign of dissent from the fate to which his defiance had consigned them. Thus, strangely, it struck the Seleucid warden that not he, but really Mattathias, had delivered the ultimatum. And though he could not grasp, in words or ideas, the alternatives of this stern promise, Apelles felt deeply certain that it was something of which he must be afraid.

So he could not order his soldiers to kill the people of Modin. Concealing his fear behind an explanation that to kill them would eliminate a fair source of the tax revenues for which he was responsible, Apelles tried to persuade individuals in the crowd of townspeople to perform the quick ritual which would merely separate them from their history. With threats, with sly blandishments, with offers of tax concessions and outright payments in gold and silver Apelles tempted them toward sacrilege. But between the crowd and the altar stood Mattathias, his fierce piety both an inspiration and a warning to those who might otherwise weaken. And by all of Apelles' words, the people of Modin could not be moved.

It seemed inevitable to Apelles that he would have to kill them all.

57

But as the realization grew, so did his fear. If he could make but one of them, just one, bend to his will, then he could believe in his power over Mattathias—and over that greater force which seemed to inhabit earth in the spirit of the man. But not until then could he find the courage to kill the rest.

So desperately Apelles sought for that one willing listener, but in vain. Even when he took children from their mothers and swore to cut their throats unless one Jew sacrificed to Apollo, the mothers and all the people they stood among only turned to Mattathias. And seeing the ultimatum restated in his eyes, they turned back to Apelles with frozen stares, prepared to witness the innocents' murder. Then Apelles, raging within an invisible dungeon, could do nothing but furiously fling his hostages to the ground and watch them crawl away, unable to raise his sword or even to cry out an order to his soldiers.

He saw his own trembling shadow grow longer, creeping back away from Mattathias, an omen of absurd defeat. And his threats became harsher, his bribes and promises more extravagant. But still the people of Modin stood firm, and Apelles could feel now the breath of that moment when he would have to decide between massacre or retreat—either way condemning himself to a lifetime of haunted hours.

Then suddenly a voice called out to Apelles, a voice from behind Mattathias, and a man started to come forward through the crowd. He was, he said, responding to the promise of gold. But through his reasoned words sliced a mysterious soundless note—ghosts shrieking out of his soul in frustration and defiance and hysterical yearning. The people of Modin had known this man to be attendant to the rituals of his faith; but also he had often asked them unanswerable questions. Was he a Jew because he had been born to Jews and lived among them, because he spoke their language and worshipped a God whose divine deeds had been performed only for fabled ancestors? Or was he a Jew because God had especially made him one, had molded in some unique way his mind and soul and conscience? How long could he—could any man—sustain himself without this knowledge, without some proof of God's existence?

His need for it had culminated in the dare he flung at God's servant, Mattathias. If the God in which he had blindly believed for so long truly existed, then let Him appear to enforce the Adon's vow. Alone Mattathias could not prevent him from reaching the altar. Eighty armed men stood ready to guarantee the act; at Apelles' order they had closed in to protect the man as he moved toward the ritual stone.

Mattathias had not hurled himself against the soldiers, had not charged at them with drawn sword. He had waited until the faithless Jew had taken the dagger given him by Apelles and raised it over his head, poised for the sacrifice. Then, in a firm, penetrating voice, Mattathias had bidden the man to stop.

She remembered the look on the man's face in that second when he had turned from the altar and glared at Mattathias—challenge carved into every feature. It was too late for him to stop. He had turned back, away from all his people, and plunged the knife down into the goat's heart.

Then, with measured steps, the Adon had begun to walk forward. As he came the soldiers raised sharp steel against him, but fell back from his path, their arms, their every sense numbed by some unseen force. Was it only a spell cast by his eyes, blue-hot with righteous anger? Apelles himself stood transfixed by the spectacle of this one man brazenly brushing through a thicket of swords as though they were no more than so many bothersome nettles.

The man at the altar watched calmly as Mattathias approached. His offending arm hung limply at his side, blood falling onto his tunic from the knife in his hand. He made no effort to deflect the strong arms which reached out and grasped his shoulders. He knew he would be powerless against the Adon, as he had seen the soldiers to be. Without resistance he surrendered himself to the judgment of the force he had challenged. And when Mattathias dashed him to the ground he fell hard, his hand curling under his body and the blade cleaving through to his heart.

But he had lived long enough to defy Mattathias. And, taking this as an omen from his own gods, Apelles felt himself freed from the terror which had paralyzed him. He shouted at the soldiers, trying to wrench them out of the stupor into which they had been thrown by Mattathias' display of chilling courage. When he saw that they responded slowly, wearily, he became enraged. His voice curdled in his throat as he ordered them to attack and kill every man, woman and child of Modin; and the lethal demand emerged as only an insane, garbled screech.

Then this horrible noise was cut dead. Mattathias' son Judah had leapt forward and slain Apelles. The Seleucid's blood was wending across dry ground toward the soldiers, red liquid fingers reaching for help. But just as it was too late to save Apelles, it was too late for the soldiers to save themselves. The Adon's other sons had sprung upon them, close behind Judah. The people of Modin, too, had suddenly appeared with weapons. The crooks of shepherds, the scythes of farmers, and women's small implements for cooking and making clothes were being wielded in their hands. And one by one the enemy fell, drowning in a sea of slashing vengeance.

From the clear vision of Mattathias' five sons leading the people of Modin against the troop of soldiers, she entered into one of the dark rooms of memory. Only myriad glints of sun on swinging metal strung the way back into full-remembered day. And there she saw Mattathias, walking with severe majesty through the human litter of enemy dead, leading his sons, the people of the town—leading her— away from the bleeding earth of Modin and into the wilderness.

The wilderness had been her home for three years. Now she dreamed of returning to her small house of wood and white clay, and living more peacefully than ever before. On the day she and her people had left Modin, she had thought they were escaping from a merciless retribution for their small revolt. But since that time she had seen that their revolt was not small—and that they had not been fleeing from death, on that day, but had been laying siege to life. Perhaps the siege was over. Perhaps not. But whether the flame in the Temple lived forever or died, something within told her the miracle continued: men would go on seeking freedom and peace from generation to generation, ignoring the insinuations of all time past that they could never achieve these total harmonies of men with men, and men with God. And someday, she thought, men would find their way to this perfect state. Though they might not always see the light of hope with their eyes, it burned eternally and its promise would always glow from the window of some fortress in paradise.

THE
SIXTH
NIGHT

It was the first cool fire he had ever known. He had passed close
to it and had felt no heat. Only light came forth from the holy lamp,
banishing darkness out of the Temple, out of the spirit of its audience. Unlike all the other fires which had blazed within his reach,
this one invited men only to serve God, not to serve themselves.

He had been raised to find his livelihood in fire. To Galilee, where
he had been born, his ancestors had brought the skill which his
father had handed down to him, step by step almost—it seemed—
from the day of his birth. As a child, and as a man, he had heaped
white sand into a large earthen chamber pulsing with vicious leap-
ing flames, had watched the fire embrace the sand until it turned
into a molten liquid. Then he had dipped a long hollow tube of metal,
or charred hardwood, into the soft, gleaming mass, scooping some
of it up on one end; the other end of the long shaft he brought to
his lips. A thousand, a thousand thousand times he had seen the
force of his breath billowing a formless iridescent pulp into a clear
hollow bubble. The act was part of him, the knowledge of its several
parts residing not in his brain, but in his lungs, his lips, his fingers—
even in his skin, which had known the heat of his family's ancient
roaring furnace every day of his life until three years ago. Once he
returned to Galilee, it would not take him long to be the master of
his trade again.

During the past three years as well, he had worked over raging
fires. But they had risen over different stones and had served a different purpose. Into these fires he had inserted all the broken, vagrant

63

bits of metal he could collect from those like himself who had followed the Maccabees into the wilderness. And, finding new skill in his hands, he had managed to provide many swords to be raised against the more finely fashioned weapons of their enemies.

He himself had wielded a sword in battle, commanded by Judah Maccabee. The same hands he had used to turn the dead powder of the earth into things of beauty had not only learned to make objects of raw ugly power, but to use them for sending new dead dust back into the earth. He had become frightened of his hands, of the destruction of which they were capable.

It was a great distance from the barren mountains rising above the Jordan Valley, where Mattathias had found shelter for his homeless people, to Galilee, where this man had first heard his captain's name. It did not seem possible for a man's name to be carried so far across a land without his being in league with the winds. To this craftsman of Galilee, who had bitterly suffered many indignities because he was a Jew, the name itself had sounded as a rallying call. And he had set out to find and to serve the man.

Across wastelands and over rocky peaks, through green valleys and along singing coils of crystal water, he had walked for many days. He had passed, too, through many small villages. And in each he would hear the beckoning name repeated—often, more and more as he came closer to its source. Mattathias was then taking his sons into the villages of Judea, tearing down the profane altars erected by Antiochus' decrees, and exhorting the Jews to uphold their ancient law. But word had traveled not only of the old man and his sacred mission; the people spoke also of the tall warrior who stood always at the old man's shoulder. Something about him, it was said, gave the people the courage they had always lacked before to defy the king's unholy edicts.

In the first days of his journey, the man from Galilee had walked his questing path alone. But as he drew nearer to Modin, and to the wilderness into which its people had fled, he met with others who had been called out of their small distant villages by a name. And on the roads there were many, too, who had come away from Jerusalem. His trek had taken him through the once magnificent city and he knew that almost all of its Jews were gone. Now it was glutted with strange peoples—Bedouin merchants, Syrian mercenaries, Phoenician sailors, Egyptians, Greeks, Arab nomads. The streets were teeming. And yet they were empty, deserted of all the people who had loved the city and whose pride had built it up into greatness. So the laws which they had made to insure its greatness were ignored. Thieves and pimps and murderers roamed everywhere, preying on one another. The city had become a corpse, its last living cells of decency succumbed to a huge, swarming infestation of maggots. Together with those who had escaped from this horror—and with all those Jews who were fleeing from the abominations inflicted on them everywhere throughout the kingdom—the man from Galilee covered the last barren ground of his search for Judah Maccabee.

To secure his followers against pursuit by an overwhelming horde of the king's soldiers, Mattathias had led them deep into a hostile land. Beyond parched, treeless plains, into treacherous ravines between sheer rock faces, through swamps which seemingly longed to leech out the strength of their desire for freedom, the Adon had brought his people to the Wilderness of Ephraim. And all those who sought to join him there had first to fight their way through all these savage obstacles imposed by nature. Still many came, like the man from Galilee. But they were altogether too few to go out again from the wilderness and hope to survive against the forces Antiochus would set upon them.

And even while they waited to accrue a great enough force, their number was diminished. So fierce was Antiochus' anger against these rebellious Jews, that he had ordered his soldiers to track them into the wilderness and there to liquidate them. When the king's troops had come upon the Jews they had not attacked immediately. They were mindful of the easy strategy which Appollonius had employed to massacre them in the streets of Jerusalem. And so they waited until the Sabbath day, when the Jews could not lay hold of their swords without violating their holy writ. Indeed, as the law was known to them, on that sacred day the Jews could do nothing to defend themselves.

But for the fact that the Seleucids were strangers to a terrain which

their victims had now come to know, they would have slain them all. As it was, one thousand Jews perished before the day waned and the soldiers went away.

Then Mattathias had called his people together—those who had survived the onslaught. They were confused and dispirited by the ancient provision which asked of them that they stand unarmed while an army descended upon them. And he knew that unless they were given the right to make a defense, their fight to keep the way of the Lord in all other things was doomed. Other armies would come against them on other Sabbaths until they were, all of them, struck down without recourse. Then would their righteous way disappear from the earth, for who was there to fight for it after they were gone? To save the law of the Lord they must depart from the law of the Lord—from that which asked them to throw away their lives for nought. And so Mattathias bid his people to take up their swords in self-defense, on whatsoever day their enemies might attack.

When it was known throughout the kingdom that the Jews had thus provided to assure their survival, those who were charged to uphold the king's commandments hesitated to go again into the wilderness. And there the Jews gathered strength, growing vastly in number as the story of their resistance reached out and inspired others.

A day came at last when Mattathias saw that his people need no longer fear to venture out through Judea. What at first had been only a small band of fearful followers had swelled to a sizable dedicated army. Now they might think not only of destroying every pagan altar in the land, but of routing all the persecutors that Antiochus had put over them—out of their homes, out of the Temple.

But Mattathias knew also that he would not be the one to lead them to this task. He had led them into the wilderness and guided them through hardship until they were ready for battle. In this endeavor he had spent his vigor unsparingly, and now he felt the life in his body spinning away to its final ebb. It would be for another to lead them back to victory.

So he summoned all his sons around him, and all the great multitude of Jews who had come into the wilderness in search of a leader. And he told them that the time was upon them when they must take the land out of the hands of their enemies and rebuild all that had been torn down. He told them, too, that not he but another man would show them the way in this difficult mission.

The man from Galilee vividly remembered that night when he had heard these words from Mattathias. He had stood in a crowd of thousands, seeing thousands more camped on the surrounding hillsides. The fires which they had built to ward off the cold, and the wildcats and jackals that prowled through the night, had clotted in his sight into a hot yellow glacier flowing down out of the mountains. Only where the Adon stood with his sons was there a dark circle of ground.

Still he was clearly visible at its center, his eyes blazing like coals with reflected flame as his lips pronounced the name his people had come to hear. The name which they had already heard, a long time before, called up from their hearts: Judah Maccabee.

Now, three years later, that mighty warrior had brought the man from Galilee, as one of many, back into the Temple. He, too, was a witness to the cool fire of the holy lamp.

But it seemed to the man from Galilee, who had lived all his life in the presence of fire, that Judah alone looked into the miraculous sacred flame as if somewhere, sometime, he had seen its kind before.

And as he thought back across the span of years to the night when the young and mighty warrior had heard the fate of his people given into his hands, the glass blower knew that Judah Maccabee had seen the cool fire even then—had seen it ever since.

THE SEVENTH NIGHT

A world of free men.

A world of nations in harmony.

A world without pestilence, flood and famine.

A world without war.

The promise of this world was in the flame—the hope. But Judah knew it was not a promise for now, for his time. It was a promise for the future.

His people had fought many battles to regain the Temple. Rivulets of blood flowed down from all the summits of their victory. Without the miracle they had witnessed for seven days, these crimson rivers would still criss-cross the fields of conscience; these would always be the first and final battlefields of wars made in the name of peace. The people of the Temple had needed the holy light to rest their doubts, to reassure them.

But it was not a second sun; it did not turn the night into day. It was no more than a beacon along a stretch of dark and deserted road, a signal to those who traveled its way that their direction was true. The road wended again into darkness. Somewhere beyond these seven days, Judah knew, the light would fade.

He wanted to believe that now his people were free, that now their wars were over, but he could not. He longed to grasp the handle of a plow, and lay down the furrows in a field of rich earth. But he knew that he would still need the strength of his arms to lift a sword, that he would plan strategies on a battleground before he plotted boundaries around a pasture. There were still enemies to imperil the

71

Jews. And they would not be deterred by the alliance with divine power that Judah and his people saw expressed in the flame. To those who hated the religion of Israel, the miracle in the Temple would appear as merely a laughable trick. God, Himself, was little more than a capricious magician in their eyes. And through Judah, they had challenged Him again and again, confident of a time, eventually, when His tricks would fail.

The first adversary Judah had faced after leading the Maccabees out from their haven in the wilderness had been Apollonius. He was then governor over Judea, an honor bestowed upon him by Antiochus as a reward for the cunning he had displayed in his successful massacre of the Jews of Jerusalem. As governor, Apollonius was in command of the great number of Macedonian troops garrisoned throughout Judea. But to assure his success over the Maccabees, the last paltry vestige of Jewish resistance, he had called upon the armies of other Syrian governors in nearby kingdoms before riding forth to do battle.

Thus victory had appeared a certainty to Apollonius as he came against the forces of the Maccabees, so small that only their proud members might call them an army. Yes, they had sufficient strength to go through isolated villages, ousting the undefended Syrian functionaries, and even the smaller garrisons. But against a mass of trained soldiers commanded by a shrewd and ruthless general, it was certain that the Maccabees would last scarcely long enough to call their defense a battle, much less to win it.

This belief had been in Apollonius' thoughts at the moment Judah had fallen upon him and smote him. After Judah had slain Apollonius he had taken the general's sword and ridden his horse through the Syrian ranks, brandishing the steel of their dead leader. And they had scattered in many directions, fleeing in terror from the enemy which, only a short time before, they had viewed with disdain.

The Maccabees had garnered their first significant victory as a coherent fighting force. And Judah had proved himself, in his first test, a supreme commander: fearless, skillful and inspiring. As these truths spread across the land, other Jews came forth to join Judah's army. Flushed with victory, their numbers increasing daily, it had occurred to the Maccabees that perhaps they were strong enough to discourage their enemies from warring further against them. And if the size and the spirit of their army were not by themselves ample deterrents, surely they were not to be ignored when coupled with the legend that was building around their captain.

It was from him that they had taken their name; he alone had been called Maccabee—"the hammerer"—before any of his brothers or any of his soldiers. Exceptionally tall and comely, he seemed to be as much a vision as a man of flesh and blood when he passed in the sight of his people, carrying the captured sword of Apollonius. The scene expressed more to the Jews than the fortunate outcome of a single battle. It verified their belief in the inevitable triumph of good over evil. All of them throughout the land spoke of it in this way, and Judah's soldiers spoke of it in this way. And soon Judah as well had begun to believe that the enemies of his people would shrink from further battle.

But he had been wrong. His desperate desire for peace had disarmed him. That was clear now, as he thought back over the many battles which had brought him at last to stand again in the Temple. It would be making the same mistake to regard the flame as a symbol of all promises fulfilled, rather than as a sign from God that vigilance would continue to be necessary in living safely through the days ahead. Judah recalled how the very elements which he had believed would discourage his enemies were those which had most incited their ambition for glory in battle. They had welcomed the bravery and determination which the Maccabees had evinced in their victory over Apollonius. It had amused the Syrians to think that, instead of a mere handful of bedraggled undisciplined farmers, they would have a diligent military force to contend with—not so large as to frighten them, only large enough to provide an entertaining amount of resistance. And so all those who sought favor and greater riches from Antiochus had vied with each other to collect armies and please the king by eliminating those who defied his commands. Thus, in the wake of the Maccabees' first victory, their enemies seemed to multiply rather than disperse.

And finally Seron, a Syrian prince, had come into the kingdom of Judea leading a large force of cavalry and swordsmen. He had marched through the land to the foot of the mountain where the Maccabees were said to shelter themselves. There he had waited for them to appear, confident of a quick success in the task which had ended for Apollonius in crushing defeat.

Looking down from their mountain haven, Bethhoron, the beleaguered Jews had watched the movement of a long dark vein over the skin of the earth until, directly below them, it had reformed into a vibrating field of men and horses and flags and reflected sun. Then they had turned their eyes, clouded with grave doubt, to Judah. How could they dare descend the mountain to face this enemy? Although their number was greater now than it had been at the time of their first battle, still they were no match for the army of Seron. They would surely perish, and with them would go the hope of restoring their people to the Temple.

But they had gone down to face the enemy, and they had been returned to the Temple. As he looked into the flame, Judah recalled the words which had come to him at Bethhoron to hearten his people—words which had risen up out of him into the air with the same inexplicable surge of the light rising out of the holy lamp:

It is no hard matter for many to be shut up in the hands of a few; and with the God of Heaven it is all one, to deliver with a great multitude, or a small company. For the victory of a battle standeth not in the multitude of an host, but strength cometh from heaven.

The soldiers of Seron's army had been forced to look up into the sun to see the Maccabees advancing upon them down the mountainside. Splinters of light had stabbed at their eyes from spaces between the dark, shifting silhouettes. And each moving figure had been refracted into an illusion of several so that the outnumbering army had believed itself to be overrun. They had scrambled frantically to save themselves, fleeing in disorder across the plains. Then Judah had taken all of his men in pursuit of the escaping enemy, and they had struck down hundreds. Seron and the other survivors—although even these outnumbered their pursuers—had run for refuge into the land of the Philistines.

Now again the Maccabees hoped that their antagonists had been totally discouraged and that a time of peace would prevail when they could rally all the people in the land into a restoration of their faith. But the days ahead were to offer the Jews only another, greater threat to their existence.

When Antiochus had learned of Seron's failure, he had determined to send a new army against the Jews, an army so mighty that even if all the able men of Israel were to come together in defense, they would still be overwhelmed. He had proclaimed this intention through all his empire, offering increased amounts of gold to all who would come into his service. And to those who had answered the call, he had dealt out a full year's pay, so that they would stand ready to march at any advantageous moment, and then to lay siege for as long as should be necessary to secure victory.

These measures had unexpectedly exhausted the king's treasury, but such was his unreasoning wrath against the Jews that he would countenance no delay in his plans. He resolved to take half of his army into Persia in quest of new wealth, while the other half was sent into Judea. Although the battle might not be won with the same satisfying swiftness, Antiochus was certain that even half of the great army he had assembled could easily achieve the desired end: total annihilation of Israel's people. Merely this part of the total force included forty thousand foot soldiers, seven thousand cavalry and scores of elephants.

The army was given into the command of three generals—Ptolemy, Nicanor and Gorgias—and they had brought it to the plains of Judea to encamp at Emmaus. There around them, like barnacles attached to the wallowing hull of a giant ship, had clustered traders from every part of the empire; certain of the superiority of the king's army, they awaited the opportunity to buy the vanquished Jews of Judea for the profitable traffic in slaves.

At Mizpah the Maccabees had prayed for strength to keep their people out of bondage. This place had been the site of the Jews' ceremonial assemblies in the ancient times before the building of the Temple. Worshipping here, because the Temple did not exist for them while it housed pagan idols, Judah felt as if the world had spun backward, whirling his people into the past. And for him to lead them to victory over the great hostile horde which awaited the Maccabees at Emmaus had seemed no less a task than to take the world in his own hands and set it spinning again in the right direction.

He had not retreated from launching this grim ordeal, and yet he had felt an unfamiliar, caustic sensation attempting to eat through the wall of older, stronger, prouder emotions he had built around his resolve. What was this strange corrosive feeling? Fear? Yes, it was some kind of fear, he realized. But it was not for himself he was afraid. It was for those men around him whom he saw trying to hide their trembling hands, and drawing their cloaks around them as if already they had been chilled by the cold winds of eternal night. He was afraid for those who were afraid, for those who understood too little of what they were fighting for to know that, unless this next battle were won, life for the Jews was to be more fearsome than death. And as Judah wished to be rid of his fear for the fearful, he reminded them of the law of his people which said that all those who were building houses, or planting vineyards, or had betrothed wives, or had no heart for combat, should not be pressed into battle. There were many to whom this law applied, but only the fearful men went from Judah's side. Those who remained to march down with him from Mizpah had all shared his bold awareness of the brutal challenge to come—and his defiance of the cruel result which fate seemed anxious to foist upon them. Waiting for the morning to come, in the camp they had established on the south side of Emmaus, Judah had said:

It is better for us to die in battle than to behold the calamities of our people and our sanctuary.

He had only given voice to the wordless speech that everyone of the Maccabees had heard that night in his heart.

Morning had not yet come when Judah had suddenly commanded

76

his men to take up their swords and depart quickly from the encampment. He had received word that the Syrian general Gorgias had left Emmaus with a contingent of five thousand men. Though this raiding party was only a fraction of the huge Syrian force, had they caught the Maccabees off guard they would easily have slaughtered them.

They did not succeed, however, in surprising the Maccabees. The camp into which Gorgias fearlessly led his soldiers contained only empty tents; the fires around them had already cooled down to the last failing embers. In the time since they had been warned, the Maccabees had been able to cover almost as much ground as Gorgias. Now, as the Syrian general set out from the Jews' deserted camp, determined to find and destroy them before the sun rose again, Judah and his men arrived very near to Emmaus, within sight of the Syrian campfires.

And there they were arrayed for battle when the first sharp edge of day cut through the purple rind of night sky and began peeling it back above the plains.

Through the night the Seleucid sentries had strained to catch the first glimpse of a messenger coming from Gorgias with news of victory. When dawn broke on the plains of Emmaus to reveal the Maccabees in their total strength, the Seleucids were terrified. Assuming that Gorgias had perished with all his men, and that the Maccabees had arrived to destroy the remainder of the invading army, the Syrian soldiers were all the more terrified to see that the Maccabees numbered only three thousand! Would they have dared to confront the Syrian camp if all the fantastic legends of their prowess—the legends which the Seleucids had ridiculed—were not true? Had they not written a new legend on the night just ended, repelling the surprise attack of a force almost twice the size of their own? And had they not come brazenly then to attack an even greater number of their enemy? Many of the soldiers of Nicanor and Ptolemy had needed no more proof than this of the Maccabees' fierce abilities, and they had fled at once. Those who had remained with their generals to raise steel against the fearsome Jews had done so with quaking arms, and so they had been no match for them.

Three thousand soldiers of Antiochus' army had been slain and all the rest routed before Gorgias had been alerted, by the din of battle and the smoke of burning tents, to return to Emmaus. Seeking the best tactical advantage, he had marched his men to a position in the mountains above the embattled Syrian camp, from where they might swoop down upon the Jews. These were the very tactics which Judah had used successfully at Bethhoron; it gave Gorgias a special satisfaction to think that Judah would be outsmarted by his own strategy.

But when the soldiers under Gorgias' command had climbed up the mountain and looked down upon the scene below, it comforted them not to see how small was the army of Judah. For they could see too all the injury and death that this "unimpressive" army had inflicted. The Syrian camp was in ruins, and the bodies of all those who had tried to defend it were strewn lifeless over the red ground. Stunned, the Seleucid soldiers would not heed Gorgias' command to descend upon the Jews. They stayed on the mountain, looking down upon the carnage and chaos below, until they saw Judah reforming his followers for a new engagement with the enemy they had sighted above them. Only then did the Syrians stream down out of the mountain, and flee away from Judea into another land.

The enormity of this triumph convinced the Jews anew that their peace would be undisturbed in all the days to follow. Would any other tyrant dare to assault the warriors who had been able to drive off or destroy ten of the enemy for every one of their own number? Judah alone realized that there needn't be any *other* tyrant. Antiochus was still alive; because his generals had failed, his hatred had not diminished. It seemed to Judah that it would not be long before his people were faced again with a deadly adventure. And even in his sleep he listened for the sound of hurried footsteps—the arrival of a messenger to inform him that the Jews were imperiled again. Only when a season of planting had passed to a season of harvest had Judah begun to think—to allow himself to think—that, perhaps, there might be a lasting peace.

However, the survivors of the battle at Emmaus had drifted back to their homes in the Seleucid kingdom; and although the shame of

their defeat haunted them and they spoke of it little, there were a few who had described the ignominious efforts of the Seleucid soldiers to Lysias. This was the general whom Antiochus had set over his kingdom while he was abroad in Persia. Lysias was jealous of the power he had attained, and feared that it would be soon stripped from him if Antiochus should learn that the Jews were still free in Judea. So he spared no effort to rally an even greater army than that which had proved itself insufficient at Emmaus. If ten men to every Maccabee were not a sure enough guarantee of victory, then there would have to be twelve men for every one, fifteen. And more horses than before, and more elephants. The money that Antiochus sent to his treasuries from Persia was all funneled out again into the hands of mercenaries until Lysias had assembled an army of sixty thousand foot soldiers and a cavalry which, by itself, outnumbered the Maccabees.

A cry of anguish had reverberated through Judah's innermost being when he heard of the new threat to the Jews. As if his former courage had been some rare element quarried from his spirit, he felt now that there was a yawning cavern within him into which he might cry for courage, only to be answered by this anguished echo. And yet he went on calling, digging deeper into himself for the courage without which he could not face his people. And at last he felt he could go forth to serve them, by commanding them.

How the Maccabees had won at Bethsur—where they had engaged the forces of Lysias—Judah was not certain. They had come this time with ten thousand men, and so the odds were more favorable than they had been at Emmaus; still, they might have been overrun without difficulty. Yet they had won. Judah could not have redrawn the strategy on a map, nor recounted a single incident which marked the victory: the brutalities of war were not something he wanted to remember tonight as he stood in the place to which war had returned them. It was a holy place. A place for prayer.

The prayer. It came to Judah now as he knelt before the flame, came to him along with the knowledge that sometime, somewhere, he would need the spirit of these words again—the words he had spoken to his men before they had all gone together to Bethsur:

Blessed art thou, O Saviour of Israel, who did quell the violence of the mighty man by the hand of thy servant David. Shut up this enemy, too, in the hand of the people of Israel and let them be confounded in their power. Make them to be of no courage and cause the boldness of their strength to fall away, and let them quake at their destruction. Cast them down with the sword of them that love Thee, and let all those that know Thy name praise Thee with thanksgiving.

Whispered by many voices, the word "amen" came to Judah's ears, rolling calmly out of the dark reaches of the Temple like surf from a midnight ocean. Judah turned from the flame to see the eyes of all in the Temple focused on him. He realized, then, that he had not simply uttered his prayer in the cloister of his heart, but had spoken it aloud. Thus he had revealed to the people his belief that their trials were not over—that the flame would fade, perhaps soon.

From the sound of their response, their hushed "amen," he knew that they had understood, and that they were still his to command.

THE
EIGHTH
NIGHT

Just as Judah's prayers, spoken at the brink of each of their bygone battlefields, had always made his people feel closer to God, his prayer before the flame had brought a revelation to all those in the Temple. They understood now that the miracle would not last forever, that it was not a preface to a world in which divine power circumvented the demands of nature and turned back all darkness. They saw clearly that their future would not be devoid of the trials which had marked their past. They also knew, however—knew in previously undiscovered corners of their minds and spirits—that if they trusted in the way of the Lord, His protection would be constant, and ultimately the greatest storms would give way to calm, and the greatest trials would end in triumph.

With this revelation, a feeling of exultation had been released, a pure joy which had hitherto been stunned into insensitivity by the awesome prospect of Eden restored. They were not sure that they were worthy of the gift of perfect life; each of them knew of the secret doubts which had always occurred to him in troubled times. If it were not for the inspiration of men like Eleazar, of women like Hannah, and of leaders like Judah, would they even have kept their faith? They were uncertain of their claim to all of the greatest gifts which they prayed to be granted by the Lord. It was far easier to rejoice in a gift deserved: the chance to earn peace by showing Him an unwavering faith in the days ahead. And so the Jews took these days of the miracle to be not only a time for solemn prayer, but a time for celebration.

They decorated the Temple with all the splendid trappings that they could find there in Jerusalem, all the holy vessels of gold which the Seleucids had left behind in their flight from the city after the Maccabees' victory over Lysias. Finely wrought chalices and plates were placed upon the altar—and menorahs, the traditional seven-branched candelabra. Then, for each of the seven nights that the lamp had burned, a candle was lit. And when the day of these preparations passed into the eighth night of the flame, one Jew who was a worker in silver and gold took the old menorah and created out of it a new one, with eight branches, especially to commemorate this magnificent occasion.

On this night a glad spirit suffused the atmosphere of the Temple, a swelling cloud of elation which could not be contained within its walls. And rather than spend the night before the flame in watchful anxiety about its future—and theirs—the people held their services and then returned into the streets of the city. There they danced and sang and laughed and rejoiced to be alive, marveling at the human miracle of finding themselves capable of such sweet pleasure after having passed through so much horror.

The priest of the Temple who, eight nights before, had lit the holy lamp from one small jar of oil, had remained in the Temple to offer a special prayer. As he finished, and raised his bowed head to look at the altar, he noticed that the holy flame was no longer burning. The sanctuary was still bright with the light of the eight candles which had been kindled in celebration of the miracle, but the particular golden hue which had tinged the air for the past eight days and nights was gone.

And yet he did not feel panic, or even sorrow. For although he could no longer see the earthly phenomenon of the flame, he knew that its source was eternal. It was not the small flickering tongue of fire by which the people had been moved, but the assurance of heavenly guidance it represented. Thus the people did well to celebrate, the priest thought, and so he did not go out of the Temple to tell them that the flame burned no more. He lowered his head and offered another prayer of thanks to God, even as he listened to the faint joyous sound of song and laughter that penetrated into the Temple from the city around it.

He did not pray alone. Another man had entered the Temple and moved slowly toward the altar at the heart of the great chamber. His head was bowed—in reverence, partly, but also because he was afraid to look at the walls. Once he had seen the shadow of death dance violently across these walls.

This was the man who had fled from the Temple after seeing one of its priests, the corrupt Lysimachus, murdered there. This was the man who had become one of the letzim, one of those who had forsaken the religion of their fathers to take up the religion of their enemies. This was the man who had stood for the past eight nights under a fig tree in a far corner of the Temple courtyard, drawn to the sanctuary by the miraculous flame he beheld through its open doors, and still repelled by the unholy memories his mind would not relinquish. Now he had come back into the Temple. The lure of the flame had brought him again to its altar.

Even before this moment he had wanted to return—ever since he had seen the flame. But because he had been one of the letzim—a faithless Jew—he believed himself undeserving of a place beside those people who had always, through all the disillusionments of their lives, been steadfast in their faith. Only now, after he had seen his people go out of the Temple to celebrate, had he entered the sanctuary to pray.

He saw at once that the flame had vanished. And yet he was not disheartened. How could he be? It was the flame that had brought him again to terms with his ancient God; it was the flame that had brought him to stand again at the source of hope. And although he could no longer look upon its beauty in the world around him, an infinity of glory was revealed to his inner eye when he began to speak the ritual words he had not said for so long.

As the night wore on, the people drifted back from the streets, one by one, to view the cause for their celebration. Each of them saw upon entering the Temple that the special glow had vanished, and yet no one cried aloud or moved to alert those outside who were still unaware. They did nothing more nor less than what they would have done had the flame still been burning. And in the late hours of the night the Temple was filled with people, all of them deep in prayer.

They were especially grateful that the miracle had lasted beyond the term of seven days. It was in that span of time that, the Bible said, the Lord had created the world and then rested from his labors. To the Jews, the eighth day of the light's duration seemed to signify the hope for a second phase of Creation, one in which man joined with God—living by his commandments—to bring the world to a new dimension of existence for all men. This future development was not a certainty—the light had not burned for a full second week. But there had at least been a sign of hope, an eighth day.

The Temple was dim when the people finished their prayers. Not only the flame from the holy lamp had flickered out; the candles of the menorah had also sent their last smoky wisps into the air. What light there was in the Temple leaked through tiny windows from the day being born outside. Still, the worshipping mass made no move to go. Something held them back, some feeling of a word left unsaid.

Then a voice rose from the shadows, the same voice which had raised them up in time of seeming futility and led them back to the Temple. And it spoke the words which freed their hearts to go forth from the scene of the vanished miracle. It was the voice of Judah, enjoining his people to remember this occasion and return always, from year to year, on the twenty-fifth day of Kislev to keep the next eight days in the Temple as a time of gladness. If this were done through all of time, the Jews would never forget how they were once delivered from annihilation. And if the future found them beset with new threats, there would be an inspiration to remain steadfast of spirit and not fall into despair.

When Judah had finished speaking, and all those in the Temple had assented, they began to leave to begin the journey back to their homes. Among them walked a woman on her way to Modin, and a man taking the first steps of a trek to Galilee. And, too, there walked the Jew who had returned from a faithless limbo as one of the letzim, and had found himself accepted again by his people in the spirit of brotherhood and forgiveness.

86

Judah was the last to go. The priest, who remained in the Temple, watched as the mighty warrior strode to the portal of the sanctuary and stopped. There he turned around for a moment and stared at the darkened altar—for just a moment. Then he grasped the spear which he had left leaning against the door, lifted it to his shoulder and walked away.

During the time of the miracle there had been time to prepare more oil for the holy lamp. The priest decanted some of this into the sacred vessel and struck the flint near the smooth surface of the liquid. And now a flame flared again from the lamp and lit the great sanctuary. But the flame was different, and its light was different.

Once again man paid tribute to God. God's brief tribute to man was gone.

THE NINTH NIGHT

He sat in his chair upon the pulpit and watched the Temple filling with people. Soft whispering brushed the air around him. The candle flames floating in rows above silver branches wavered gently; and he thought of flags flicked out by a breeze. Then a larger, unwanted thought came and scratched for entrance into his mind—a brutal animal outside a door he could never build strong enough. But tonight he let the door open, without fear. In the Temple, and because it was Chanukah, he knew he could tame his memories.

Black memories. Black. Glistening black. Boots. Bright black leather, and candles glistening out of the blackness. And flashlights. The steadiness of candle flame giving way to brief instants of flame—matches flaring (matches, as dear to some as were the children they knew they had lost forever) in boxcars. Faces recognized. Whispers. Parched voices saying prayers. Lines of his people whispering, "God."

It was history now. His story and the story of people like him who had escaped—and the story of those who had not escaped—had been written down in books. There it would survive when all the other reminders had perished. When he had died, when the barbed wire had rusted into powder, when flowers cracked through the concrete shower floors, all the ugliness would still be there in the history books. The story would be told along with the story of the Maccabees. Until, someday, the two stories would become one. The ugliness and defeat would be forgotten, the victory and beauty remembered. The eternal optimism of his people, of all men, would always keep the story of the Maccabees alive. Or was it, perhaps, that the memory

89

of the Maccabees would sustain man's hope? Hadn't he thought often of that ancient army of Jews during the years of his imprisonment? When hope had stared in at him from the other side of the barbed wire like a visitor at a zoo, hadn't the name of those long-dead heroes seemed somehow to unlock the cage?

How important it was to remember the Maccabees! If twenty-five years had passed since Hitler's crimes—and more than two thousand years since the evils of Antiochus—it was not yet enough. There were still places in this world where Jews suffered for their beliefs, where men of one kind or another were damned for the heritage into which they had been born. There were still barbed-wire boundaries behind which the strength of an idea was decided by the strength of an army.

The sweetness of song cut through the rabbi's bitter thoughts. The cantor was finishing a traditional chant. The rabbi rose from his chair and walked toward the altar, passing some of the children who had been specially seated on the pulpit for tonight's service. With these children—for these children—the rabbi hoped he could vividly portray to all of his congregation the full meaning of Chanukah. It was not merely a commemoration of one heroic event; not at all a petty, prideful celebration for the victories of past millennia. It was an imperative reconsecration of the courageous spirit that Jews might forever need to survive—that all men might forever need to overcome their own follies.

The rabbi had attempted to translate this Chanukah message into the special ceremony he had written for tonight, the eighth night of the Festival of Light. As he spoke aloud eight of the great names of Jewish history, eight children would come forward to stand at the menorah. After the rabbi had explained the significance of the first hallowed name, one candle would be lit. Then the *shamash*—the candle from which the eight festival lights take their flame—would be passed on from one child to the next. Before the eyes of the congregation, a new generation of Jews would rekindle the lights of faith in the name of all the generations past.

The rabbi pronounced the eight chosen names to his congregation. The sounds reverberated within the synagogue and faded away, as if they had burst out through the walls and begun a long journey. Indeed, the words rang away into silence like a call issued to eight historic Jews to leave their place in Eternity and appear before the worshippers assembled in the Temple.

Moses.

Micah.

Hannah.

Hillel.

Moses Maimonides.

Moses Mendelssohn.

Isaac Mayer Wise.

Einstein.

The congregation was silent, alert, questioning. They were puzzled by the inclusion of some of these names. Moses Mendelssohn. A brilliant man, yes—a German Jewish scholar who gave the Bible its first translation into German from the original Hebrew. But could this contribution to the Jewish heritage be honored before those of some of the prophets who had gone unmentioned—Isaiah, Amos, Jeremiah? Wasn't there, perhaps, some merit to the argument that interpreting the language of the Bible into a modern national vernacular cheapened the Jewish tradition rather than enriched it?

And in what action had Einstein evinced any desire to ennoble Judaism? Without question he had been one of the greatest scientists in history. But hadn't the brilliant theoretician foregone any formal practice of the religion into which he had been born? For all his contributions to humanity, what was there to earn him a place in the hearts of Jews ahead of other great men who had been committed to the custom and ritual that Einstein had ignored?

The congregation waited for the answers.

The rabbi intoned the first name again, quietly—no longer as if calling to a distant spirit, but as if speaking to someone standing in his presence—then he cited the achievement of the man named:

"Moses. He rose from his own enslavement to lead all of his people out of slavery. And then, having freed himself and his fellow men, he saw that freedom did not mean an end to service. There were and would always be duties owed to God and to humanity. These Moses

91

summarized in the Decalogue. Written upon tablets of stone, Moses delivered the Ten Commandments to his people at Sinai, and they have since been etched into the conscience of all mankind, from where they shall never be erased."

A child's hand brought the *shamash* to the wick of the first candle. The name of Moses inspired light to be given into the synagogue. The rabbi continued speaking:

"Micah. The prophet of Israel who set down the prescription for man's moral conduct. In the plain language of a soul beknighted by humility, he gave a fitting answer to the question which had been uppermost in all minds from the time of their spiritual awakening, What does the Lord require of thee? Only to do justly, to love mercy, and to walk humbly with thy God."

A second candle took the flame and held it.

"Hannah. A mother whose pious teachings instilled in each of her seven sons the courage to die rather than forswear their righteous traditions or profane their God. She never recanted from what she had taught them, and when the last of her sons had perished, her spirit remained unfettered by bitterness, and the name of the Lord was still sanctified in her heart.

"Hillel. He found the answer to satisfy a nonbeliever who challenged him to cull out the meaning of Judaism and speak it in a sentence, and so doing he laid the ethical foundation for another religion to be founded later by a young man from Nazareth named Jesus, who was his pupil. 'What is hateful to yourself, do not to your fellow man,' Hillel said. 'This is the whole of the Torah. The rest is but commentary.'"

Half of the menorah's branches were now tipped by flickering points of yellow. The next name spoken by the rabbi came out of a different part of history than had Hillel—more than a thousand years later. The two halves of the ceremonial candelabrum were, apparently, to represent the ancient world and the modern. The example of the ancient world had brought its light into the Temple. The candles to be lit for the inspirations of more recent times were still dark and cold.

"Moses Maimonides. His philosophical writings expanded and interpreted the gifts of simple reason which flowed from the lawgivers and prophets. The Thirteen Articles of Faith, composed by this Spanish sage after carefully examining the hundreds of statutes written down in the ancient sacred writings, are an uncompromising commitment to the strength of Judiasm. 'I believe with a perfect belief,' each of the Articles begins. The Jew who would reaffirm his faith will find the means through reciting Maimonides' stirring declarations. And the Jew who would understand his faith will find the means in another of this sage's writings—the Book of Knowledge.

"Moses Mendelssohn . . ."

The rabbi saw some of the people in the auditorium sit forward, their faces clearly indicating skepticism. Could he satisfy them about the importance of Mendelssohn? Would anyone who had not lived through the experience of being alienated and brutalized by the society around him—as he had been himself, in Germany a generation earlier—understand the importance of Mendelssohn's effort? Perhaps if this eighteenth-century German Jew had succeeded more completely in realizing his ambitions, the Jewish extermination in Nazi Germany would never have taken place.

"By translating the Old Testament into German, Mendelssohn sought to break down the ghetto walls. The Jews had been sealed away, persecuted, because the lack of communication between them and their neighbors gave rise to misunderstandings and fear. Once the most prized works in Hebrew literature were translated into the language of a country where many Jews had chosen to live, they could master it, and an important part of the Gentile world could begin to comprehend the beauty and truth inherent in Judaism's spiritual charter."

The rabbi felt gratified to see his congregation nodding agreement with his words. As the next candle was lit, they understood the importance of making greater efforts at communicating fully with their neighbors. Even among peoples of the same country, communication was still a primary source of difficulty. Rich and poor, parent and child, Negro and white had not yet established a truly successful dialogue; sometimes, even in America, they seemed to be speaking different languages. Perhaps a new kind of translator was needed.

93

Or perhaps people merely needed to start listening to each other. It was only a small beginning, the rabbi mused, for his congregation to be listening to him.

"Isaac Mayer Wise. A Jewish scholar and rabbi who emigrated to America, he absorbed the spirit of adventure that abounded in a country where frontiers still waited to be tamed. There were frontiers of faith left to be explored, too, Wise decided. Judaism did not have to remain fixed in the customs it had observed unquestioningly for thousands of years. Indeed, it might be strengthened by the elimination of outworn concepts. Out of these ideas formulated by Isaac Mayer Wise came the movement for Reform Judaism. The effort to institute change was not allowed to succeed easily. For many years he stood alone in his fight against those who could countenance no alteration of the practices honored by time, if no longer by reason. But Wise was as resolute in his fight—albeit as outnumbered—as the Maccabees had been in theirs. And, like the Maccabees, Isaac Mayer Wise triumphed."

There were numerous smiles visible in the audience. These Jews did not have to be told of Wise's victory. Theirs was a thriving Reform congregation, determined to keep its outlook modern.

And yet they were not modern enough to accept unquestioningly as a contributor to the Jewish heritage the man whose name the rabbi now spoke.

"Albert Einstein. His theories about the universe mark him as a prophet. Although he may have neglected the formal worship of the synagogue, we can only wonder if he did not do so in order to make his way more clearly to his own vision of God. Does that make him less a Jew? It is written in our sacred books that the effort to come to terms with the incomprehensible is a private experience. Einstein's definition of the universe was, in part, a private confrontation with a cosmic God. If Moses could talk with God in a burning bush, Einstein could talk with Him through his formulae. The great scientist was truly a prophet, and his vision will furnish light for us all through the ninth night of Chanukah."

In his notes, the rabbi had written a few final lines to clarify for his audience what he had meant by "the ninth night of Chanukah." But as he paused to let the phrase penetrate, the congregation whispered in unison the word that signified they had already arrived at understanding . . . "Amen."

The rabbi signaled for the Chanukah hymn to begin and returned to his seat. He looked out over his congregation and searched the faces he saw there. Had they truly comprehended the meaning of his final words? The ninth night of the original Chanukah was the time when the Jews might again have wondered, with the vanishing of the flame, if God had deserted them. Instead it marked the beginning of a new dedication, a new determination to trust in the existence of God no matter what hardships might be visited upon the Jews in all the times to come. In that sense, the ninth night had never ended.

If his people understood that, the rabbi thought, then they would be able to meet all the challenges which would inevitably rise up between now and the time they dreamed of—the time they were singing about as they reached the end of the Chanukah hymn—a time "which will see, all men free . . . tyrants disappearing."

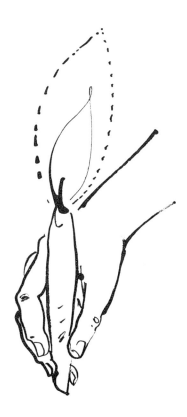